The March of
Mobile Money

The March of Mobile Money

THE FUTURE OF LIFESTYLE MANAGEMENT

SAM PITRODA & MEHUL DESAI

COLLINS BUSINESS

An Imprint of HarperCollins*Publishers*

First published in India in 2010 by Collins Business
An imprint of HarperCollins *Publishers*
a joint venture with
The India Today Group

ISBN: 978-81-7223-865-0

2 4 6 8 10 9 7 5 3

Sam Pitroda and Mehul Desai assert the moral right
to be identified as the authors of this work.

HarperCollins *Publishers*
A-53, Sector 57, Noida 201301, India
77-85 Fulham Palace Road, London W6 8JB, United Kingdom
Hazelton Lanes, 55 Avenue Road, Suite 2900, Toronto, Ontario M5R 3L2
and 1995 Markham Road, Scarborough, Ontario M1B 5M8, Canada
25 Ryde Road, Pymble, Sydney, NSW 2073, Australia
31 View Road, Glenfield, Auckland 10, New Zealand
10 East 53rd Street, New York NY 10022, USA

Typeset in 12/18.3 Dante MT Std
InoSoft Systems

Printed and bound at
Thomson Press (India) Ltd

We would like to thank the entire C-SAM family and its well-wishers, without whom this journey would not be as enriching.

We would like to thank Mayank Chhaya, without whom we would not have been able to complete this book.

We would like to thank our better halves, Anu and Malavika, without whose companionship this journey and book would not be as meaningful.

Contents

Preface

Sitting across from her at the dining table in our Chicago home one late evening in the early 1990s, as I saw my wife, Anu, write cheques for numerous bills – groceries, gas, retail, travel, entertainment, utilities, credit cards, and others – it occurred to me that there must be a better way to do this somewhat monotonous task. I asked her how many hours on an average she spent writing cheques and paying bills every month. She replied with noticeable exasperation, 'at least eight to ten', what with my children and I having our own set of cards, everyone spending indiscriminately, some wanting airlines miles in return and others collecting loyalty points for discounts on the new fashions at department stores.

If I then added the time she would spend in screening each statement for potential fraudulent charges, organizing receipts, cutting paper coupons from the Sunday newspaper, these ten hours quickly stretched into what seemed to be a criminal waste of time, especially given all the technology and tools around us. As I watched Anu that night, it struck me that she was not alone in her frustration, and that countless other women, men and families all over the world could do so much more with their time than write endless paper cheques every month.

In the early 1970s, I had invented the digital diary, which digitized the ubiquitous paper diary in which we store our contacts, appointments, and other details that get us through our work and personal engagements on a daily basis. Several companies, such as Toshiba, Casio, Radio Shack, Sharp, and Texas Instruments, were responsible for making my invention a household commodity among people in different age groups from the US to Japan.

Little did any of us know then that the digital diary was to later evolve into the personal digital assistant or PDA hand-held computer, and eventually morph into the smart phone that would combine the PDA and mobile phone into the modern-day equivalent of the Swiss knife.

That night, as Anu continued to write cheques, I decided to solve what then appeared to be a relatively simple problem. I had just returned to the US from India after spending over a decade helping the government indigenously develop and launch a nationwide telecommunication infrastructure that would eventually lead to India's rise as a global Information Technology powerhouse. Given my background in technology, with several worldwide patents on telephony and digital switching issued to me over the years, I called my patent attorneys in Chicago and asked them to send me all the issued patents related to credit cards and electronic payments. As the rest of the family sat watching television every evening, I went over a hundred different patents issued by the US patent office, on what appeared for the large part to be inventions on chip-on-cards, or smart cards as the industry calls them.

What seemed very obvious to me was the need for a digital wallet, where, quite like the digital diary, we needed to digitize the entire leather wallet – leather jacket, plastic cards, paper receipts, et al. So now Anu, instead of buying an empty leather wallet and stuffing it with plastic cards from banks, airlines, insurance companies and so on, would buy an empty digital wallet the size of a plastic card with a touch-sensitive colour LCD screen to preserve the image and branding of these cards. She would still approach the same set of providers that sent her these plastic cards, but now request an electronic version of these cards that could be securely and wirelessly sent directly over-the-air to her digital wallet.

Once her digital wallet was loaded over the air with all the cards she typically carried around in her leather wallet, she could go out and transact. Instead of swiping a plastic card, she would now 'beam' a card using infrared, proximity radio frequency (RF) or bar-codes at a retail location or beam it over-the-air to pay a bill to a utility company, to transfer funds between bank accounts or possibly pay for a book from a web-store like Amazon. Similarly, the receipt for these transactions would now be beamed back to her digital wallet, archived electronically, and potentially used not only at tax-time but also for other user-approved or opt-in profile-driven value- added services. Not only would this simplify Anu's life, but also the settlement between the stakeholders in the value chain – numerous banks, merchants, issuers and acquirers.

With the raging debate on global warming and the damage we have done to the environment, the opportunity to significantly reduce the use of paper and plastic through this digital wallet should be incentive enough to start making the necessary changes to the infrastructure, which, as one can well imagine, would not be a simple task given the installed base of retail terminals. Assuming that there are over 4 billion plastic cards manufactured every year in the US alone, and billions of paper receipts printed in multiple copies, going all digital through paperless transactions and electronic receipts would help substantially in preserving the much-needed forest cover every year.

I filed my first patent on the mobile wallet concept in the US in 1994. This patent was issued in 1996 and set off my co-author and I on an unbelievable journey over the past sixteen years (and counting). The journey has spanned all five continents, from the top of the demographic pyramid to the bottom, resulting in our setting up commercial enterprises, and becoming the driving force behind rethinking various socioeconomic challenges that directly fuel disparity across the world.

I have said this many times in public speeches that if we had known then what we know now about the inner workings of the transaction industry the world over – and the role that big business lobbies, vested interests, money power, inertia to change, and a rigid mindset play – we would not have embarked on this journey to single-handedly take this disruptive technology forward. At the same time, just like other life-changing journeys, we would not trade this one for anything else in the world. This is where I believe ignorance and arrogance help – ignorance of complexities, bureaucracies, and fears that 'It cannot be done', and arrogance to have the inner strength and confidence that even a small, unknown person can make a difference and transform the entire industry.

The March of Mobile Money is the story of our journey and our missionary work, which started from my dining table in Chicago and continues to unfold as we uncover layer upon layer of intriguing complexities, many a time fuelling special interests. In this book we have attempted to present to the reader some background information on the three industries that have gone through major transformation in the last ten years due to the Internet, web-based services and evolving business models – namely telecommunication, banking and retail. More importantly, however, we have presented our vision of how transactions, and fundamentally, the nature of money itself, will change as we start spending bits and bytes on mobile phones. Money on mobile phones has the potential to reach 4 billion people in a very short time and benefit not only the rich at the top of the pyramid but also the unbanked poor in Africa, Asia and Latin America at the bottom of the pyramid, with micropayments, microloans and other financial services.

In the process, not only is there the promise to simplify Anu's and millions of other consumers' lives on a daily basis but also the potential to be a powerful agent of change in reducing the gap between the haves and have-nots the world over. We hope our journal, rather than being a technical reference book, becomes the inspiration for the reader to take such disruptive ideas forward and potentially change the world for the better, one mobile phone at a time!

Oak Brook Terrace,   Sam Pitroda
Illinois

Introduction

The primary thesis of this book stems from many seminal changes in the world of telephony, particularly in mobile wireless telephony, and associated implications on banks, merchants and consumers. We draw from the following points to offer a perspective on how the world of mobile telephony and secure mobile transaction opportunities will bring about a profound transformation in the manner we manage, monitor, move, mobilize and manufacture money in the future.

- The number of mobile phones worldwide is rapidly moving toward the 4 billion mark, in the process providing unprecedented access and penetration. This spread is taking in its sweep people from all walks of life, all demographics, and ethnicities. Throughout the world, in the United States, Asia, Europe, Latin America, Africa, the Middle East, people of all ages use mobile phones everywhere and all the time.

- In the last twenty years, over a trillion dollars have been spent in creating infrastructure needed to seamlessly interconnect these mobile phone users. This includes paying for the frequency spectrum, building base stations, antennae, towers, and production, distribution and delivery systems for over 3 billion mobile phone devices.

- Over the past five years, mobile phones have become very powerful and intelligent with significant processing capability, extended battery life, memory, colour displays, touch-sensitive screens, cameras, proximity communication over Bluetooth and Near Field Communication (or NFC), and multiple features and functionalities that go beyond mere voice calls and elementary data services.

- The unprecedented access and computing power in the hands of nearly 4 billion consumers with seamless global connectivity has made many businesses invest in delivering a variety of new services on mobile phones. Ranging from ring tones to stock trading to social networking, service providers have come to recognize the enormous business potential waiting to be tapped.

- In the last twenty years, banking has evolved from high-street lobbies and ATMs to web-based portals and aggregators, from chequing and savings accounts to investment portfolios and insurance products, from cheque books and credit cards to co-branded and stored-value cards, and from paper or plastic to key fobs and dongles.

- The merchants have also evolved significantly, profiling consumers and their spending behaviour, resulting in more personalized services for consumers and recurring sales for merchants. The other trend successfully launched by merchants is that of 'closed-loop alternative payment instruments' to cash or traditional cash-replacement products (like cheques or credit cards) in the form of rewards, loyalty points, frequent flyer miles or plain coupons.

- Beyond the virtual merchants and Internet-based service providers is a growing breed of social networks and online communities, which boasts of significantly large numbers of users bound by some common themes. These themes can range from posting real-life videos or exchanging professional profiles and potential sales leads to enacting an avatar in Second Life. These communities leverage the Internet as a medium to connect, transact, and evolve, and owing to their inherently segmented nature, are increasingly becoming a convenient target for advertisers and specialized service providers.

- Along with increasing efficiency at the back-end, whether through outsourcing of non-core competencies or procurement through global supply chains, telecom companies, banks and retailers have increasingly started focusing on new methods of customer acquisition, customer retention and customer service. Personalization of products and services and user-centric methodologies are now central to all service provider strategies.

- As the Internet has evolved, the magnitude of content and services provisioned through it has grown phenomenally. Searching for relevant information on the Internet, or 'Googling', has become an industry in itself, and new business models based on captive 'eyeballs' have emerged. These eyeballs for the most part are content-related, and searching for content typically leads to monetization through advertising. Almost all of the online advertising models are based on eyeballs and content. The next frontier for online advertising will be driven by transactions through mobile phones and personalized profiling.

- Service providers have been watching the spectacular

growth of the wireless industry, with the mobile phone being cited by consumers as both an indispensable tool as well as a status symbol (especially for urban youth), and are poised to leverage and exploit this channel to alleviate growing pressures on profitability and differentiation.

- Adoption and growth of mobile phones has understandably been stronger in markets with lower PC and/or Internet penetration. Service providers, especially in emerging markets and owing mainly to pricing pressures, have evolved different delivery models, resulting in disruptive business models and realignment of traditional enablers. Some of these models, which successfully scale in high-growth markets like China and India, will inevitably bring down the cost of services to the end user, and consequently can be expected to cause realignment of enablers in the well-developed markets of North America and Western Europe.

- In today's competitive environment, with telecom companies (specifically wireless operators) seeking new services to increase their Average Revenue Per User (ARPU) and differentiation, and banks trying to acquire new customers, the promise of mobile phone-based commerce is enticing operators to become banks, and vice versa. The root cause of this confusion is the desire of both operators and banks to acquire and control the consumer, in the process restricting the evolution of scalable systems and business models for mobile commerce and mobile payments.

- However, several trials and limited commercial services have been launched to provide mobile payment capabilities related to specific services such as railway ticketing, person-to-person payments, money transfer and online shopping. All these efforts have been predominantly limited by regional focus and online services designed in an environment with vertical silos, blindfolds, quick entry and short-term gains.

- In addition, the need to modify the point-of-sale (POS) terminals with NFC capabilities, and the limited availability of NFC-enabled handsets, have delayed the growth of proximity-based mobile transaction services, which constitute the bulk of the transaction revenues at merchant locations.

- Despite the confusion of roles and a lack of supporting NFC infrastructure, it is well recognized that tremendous opportunities are available today in providing secure mobile delivery channels for various services related to banking, bill payments, person-to-person transactions, money transfer, coupons, loyalty, advertising, ticketing, credit cards, debit cards, prepaid cards, gift cards, receipts, etc.

- In the last five years, significant time and resources have been invested in developing standards and launching mobile commerce experiments in different parts of the world. A handful of these experiments have been successful but have not become ubiquitous primarily due to complicated user-interfaces, limited usability, single service offering and non-scalable business models.

- The key questions of what it would take to move money on mobile phones, when it would happen, how it would unfold and become pervasive, remain of great interest to banks, operators, merchants and consumers. When this happens, what it would mean to various stakeholders, and how they will get transformed in the process, is of interest to many.

- In our judgement, the key to future success lies in creating the leather wallet metaphor, supported by innovative models of putting cash in and taking cash out of the system to provide simplicity, convenience, security, flexibility and multiple options on services and service providers with over-the-air issuance, branding, promotions, receipts, reports and various other features and functionalities integrated into one user-friendly application on mobile phones.

Money means different things to different people. To some it is a source of power, prestige, position, and status symbol. To others it is a matter of necessity, survival, income and existence. To a few it is an end in itself while to many it is a means to an end. Money is reflected in greed, generosity, philanthropy, commitment, trust, concern, etc. Money is perhaps the only instrument around which the entire range of human emotions revolves – jealousy, anger, love, compassion, rivalry and even hatred.

In the end, money keeps the world going. It is the fuel that propels the global economy. Ideally, the supply of money needs to be expanded. The uneven distribution of money creates inequality, which at times breeds contempt, violence, and wars. Banking has still traditionally remained under the control of the rich and the middle class the world over. It has not reached a large number of the poor who need micropayments and microloans.

Will mobile payment technology transform the nature of physical interaction between consumers, merchants and banks? Will it reduce the transaction costs in time and expense and lead to personalized ATMs? Will it also bring non-tradable items to trading to create markets for more things and more forms of money while dispensing with the need for intermediaries?

Will the march of mobile money lead to improved
productivity and efficiency and increased reach and richness

in applications? Will the disruptive nature of mobile money technology help provide the much-needed financial services to the unbankable and bring them to the mainstream of the global economy?

We have made an attempt to answer many of these questions, tracked various efforts to provide financial services on mobile phones, systematically reviewed the different industries that will influence as well as be impacted by this inevitable phenomenon, cited what we believe are the key factors that would enable largescale adoption and, finally, presented some of our own hypotheses and predictions.

We have also included a special chapter on India – 'The Power of a Billion Connected People' – to review the key stakeholders, the various innovative models that have been launched, and the impact mobile money will have on India – its demography, disparity, and development – moving forward.

This book is our attempt to chronicle several trends and evaluate the implications of the inevitable march of mobile money.

1

Unprecedented Connectedness

Between chomping on a Panini sandwich and sipping green tea on Wall Street, Mark quickly tracks the movement of his portfolio on his mobile phone. A few blocks away from him, sitting in her office, his wife, Catherine, is tracking their ten-year-old son's movement on her child locator at a summer camp. At their home, Catherine's teenage sister, Jodie, is sending an SMS, or Short Message Service, from her mobile phone to a friend in Tokyo to log on to her page on MySpace.com.

In Tokyo, Kasumi receives Jodie's SMS and logs on to MySpace.com and sends the link to her brother, Ichiro, just as he is waving his phone at a turnstile at a train station to pay his fare. During the ride home, he surfs the MySpace page and then books an airline ticket to Shanghai, where he is to attend a conference on mobile gaming.

In Shanghai, his host, Li Tang, receives the message even as he is topping up airtime on his phone. After quickly responding to Ichiro, Li sends the latest ring tone to his girlfriend, Imelda, in Manila, who is busy communicating with a banker in Mumbai on a payment she wired using her phone for a textile consignment.

Shireesh, the banker in Mumbai, confirms to Imelda even as he asks a colleague to send an SMS to the textile mill about the receipt of the payment. The colleague sends the SMS and books a railway ticket for her summer vacation. Shireesh then receives a 'dropped call' and knows from the caller ID that Abdul Jabbar, a concert promoter in Dubai, is trying to reach him. He calls Jabbar to tell him that his movie star client had reminded him about the advance for the upcoming show.

Jabbar says the money is on the way and then sends an email using his smart phone to Peter, a travel agent in Johannesburg, to confirm the hotel booking for the Mumbai movie star for shows in South Africa. In his spare time, Peter also supplies exotic flowers to clients in Vienna. He sends an email to Wolfgang, his client in Vienna, confirming the shipping of the flowers. Peter has a farmer friend named

Sehloho on the outskirts of Soweto, with whom he also runs a microfinance business. Sehloho has just sent him an email, using his Internet-enabled handheld device, containing a statement of accounts.

Meanwhile, in Vienna, Wolfgang receives the mail while parking his car and paying the parking fee through his mobile phone. Wolfgang then calls a dating service in Stockholm for a weekend get-together. Olof, the Stockholm contact, receives the call while buying a soda can at a vending machine using his mobile phone. He sets up the date with another client, Judy, in London and sends her Wolfgang's MMS (Multi-Media SMS Message).

Judy receives the MMS while playing poker online on her phone, confirms her visit, and then remembers she had to send a coupon from Marks & Spencer's to her bank executive friend, Mark, in New York; she sends Mark a coupon using her Internet-enabled mobile phone.

These seemingly random activities are really part of a global pattern being created every hour by mobile phones. It also reflects the process of globalization, privatization, free market economies, and development the world over. In a truly connected world, these patterns create special global communities of interest and special global user groups.

At any given time, hundreds of millions of people across the world, irrespective of their geographic locations, ethnic affiliations, race, religious preferences or cultural moorings,

3
•
•

GLOBAL CONNECTEDNESS

STOCKHOLM
Vending Machines
Dating Service
Enterprise

VIENNA
Parking
Bill Payments
Groceries

LONDON
MMS
Coupons
Gambling

TOKYO
Transit
Shopping
Airline (Ticketing)

SHANGHAI
Airtime Top-Up
Ring-Tones
Gaming

MANILA
Person-to-Person
Airtime Resell
Locator Service

MUMBAI
Missed Calls
Mobile Banking
Railway (Ticketing)

DUBAI
Money Transfer
Students Services
Tourism

JOHANNESBURG
Micro-Payments
Commodity Pricing
Hotels (Booking)

NEW YORK
Stock Trading
My Space
Child Locator

use mobile phones to connect and carry out diverse chores. Industry estimates the number of mobile phone users in the world to be close to 4 billion. This means over half of humanity uses cell phones. At the forefront of this mobile revolution are people in their teens and early twenties, whose population is well in excess of 1 billion, followed by people in every demography and age group, who use mobile phones extensively in their day-to-day lives.

Mobile phones have transformed more lives in a decade than what the fixed-line legacy phones did in a century. Unlike the legacy phones, which require users to be at a specific location, mobile phones have freed people and, in the process, empowered them in terms of convenience, time and the way they communicate and carry out their chores on their phones. That mobility has caused a dramatic shift in lifestyles around the world, not just in being able to communicate anywhere anytime but extend boundaries of social networking. That close to 4 billion people can be in touch at any given time and place has serious sociological and cultural consequences, let alone economic ones, that the world has barely begun to understand.

The predominantly young demographic profile of the mobile phone users has an enormous impact on technological innovations, convergence, business models and eventually, economies. A prime example of these shifts is the emergence of mobile music downloads as a substantial industry. Mobile music is perhaps one of the most important industries in the content market globally, generating gross revenues of $4.4 billion in 2005, about $6 billion in 2006 and nearly $8 billion in 2008; mobile music today accounts for nearly 15 per cent of the global music market.

Take another example of the ring tone economy created by mobile telephony. On the face of it, it seems like a trivial pursuit to want to have different kinds of ring tones, from pop songs to prayers, on mobile phones. But in an increasingly style-driven world, ring tones are as much a statement of individuality as the kind of mobile phones one uses. According to some estimates, the ring tone economy, barely five years old, has grown into a multibillion dollar industry worldwide.

The impressive advances in mobile phone designs, coupled with convergence of a wide variety of content and services, have created a distinct cell phone generation in the world. This generation is now shaping trends internationally. They are typically in their late teens and early twenties, comfortable with technologies and gadgets. They jump while multitasking from talking on mobile phones to music to pictures to the Internet with consummate ease. Their attention span is short, reflexes are fast, interests are broad and contacts are international. They are willing to expand and experiment. These cross platform travellers do not necessarily spend much time in front of their television sets any more. Their mobility is driving new content and applications. To be able to eat at a sushi bar, while downloading a 50 Cent video and chatting with a girlfriend, while answering questions about a work-related proposal, is an ability that this generation has begun to take for granted in their mobile devices. This is a generation that refuses to delay gratification – 'I don't know what I want but I want it now.' Not only does this population want it *now*, but it wants it *all*. Impulsiveness is a key part of their personality. They get bored easily and quickly. However, within their fluid universe, there is a certain stability and order which can be mined for great economic results.

There is a whole generation of people born after the first mobile phones came into use who have no concept of life in pre-mobile phone days. It is a measure of how widespread and essential cell phones have become that most major mobile operators offer competitively priced family plans, which include a number of phones within a family that can share their mobile minutes. Industry experts recognize that in the history of telecommunications it is now acceptable to talk about *Before Mobile Phones* (BMP) and *After Mobile Phones* (AMP). The generation that was born AMP tends to take mobile phones completely for granted. When they see a new mobile phone, they do not ask how good the audio quality is but how fast the wireless Internet surfing is or how quickly they can transfer their videos or download Rihanna's

Umbrella. Nor do they need introduction manuals to understand and operate new features and functionalities.

There is a generation of people who were born soon after cell phones came into use but well before they became such widespread and powerful tools, the kind of people who represent a link between the world of fixed-line telephony and mobile telephony. These are the people who were born about twenty years ago, when fixed-line phones had peaked and mobile phones had just begun to make their presence felt. This generation graduated from bulky instruments with unwieldy battery packs to instruments that fit in the palm of their hands. A lot of mobile users in this generation still use mobile phones as an instrument for voice exchange.

These also include the New Age knowledge workers, who have leveraged the growing capabilities of mobile phones to significantly increase their productivity and efficiency in an ever-changing world, where the lines between work and pleasure and office and home are continuously blurring. Not only are these enterprise champions pushing the envelope in terms of new applications over mobile phones, but in an increasingly global and flat world, they are exporting these new technologies to different markets around the world, in the process creating unique business models that leverage a global technology for local delivery of services. This generation of users takes mobile phones for granted, albeit for a very different set of reasons, which may start with assuming that any mobile phone worth considering must support email and scale to supporting buying stocks and groceries or paying at transit and gas stations. When they see a new mobile phone, they ask whether it will support their enterprise Virtual Private Network (VPN) or whether they can download an application to pay their utility bills.

While the youth and the early adopters across the globe are the predominant users of the ever increasing value-added services on mobile phones, there are a large number of older people who use them for 'less glamorous tasks.' On 25 August 2005, *The New York Times* reported on a mobile phone revolution unfolding in Africa. Quite dramatically, the story, datelined Yanguye in South Africa, began with thirty-six-year-old Bekowe Skhakhane, who 'does even the simplest tasks the hard way.'

'Fetching water from the river takes four hours a day. To cook, she gathers sticks and musters a fire. Light comes from candles,' the paper wrote.

'But when Ms. Skhakhane wants to talk to her husband, who works in a steel factory 250 miles away in Johannesburg, she does what many in more developed regions do: she takes out her mobile phone,' the paper said.

The news story underscored the transformative impact of mobile telephony on a society that has not moved too far from its primitive roots. For instance, the paper said one pilot programme helps about a hundred farmers in South

Africa's northeast to find out prevailing prices for produce in major markets. This knowledge is crucial for them when they sit down to negotiate with middlemen.

In another example of how cell phones are changing life and management of health-care, workers in the rural southeast use cell phones to call ambulances to distant clinics. However, the most compelling example of this change was evident in an illiterate woman living on the banks of the Congo river. Not having electricity and hence refrigeration, she kept her captured fish tethered to a string till she received an order on her cell phone.

India, with barely a few hundred thousand mobile subscribers in the mid-1990s, now has over 470 million and is adding over ten million new mobile phones every month. A striking aspect of this extraordinary growth is that most of it is now coming from smaller cities, towns and villages. With the country's mobile phone operators offering reputedly the world's lowest rates, cell phones are now being used by segments of society unthinkable even five years ago, from green grocers making less than $1000 a year to roadside cobblers earning even less. Grocers who do home deliveries in India report that cell phones have increased their customer base since people can now call them and order fresh vegetables. The economic impact of cell phones is equally felt by farmers, taxi drivers, plumbers, electricians, car mechanics, truck drivers and even priests who solemnize

10

marriages and preside over other rituals. Small and medium farmers and fishermen in India with modest landholdings, who were earlier at the mercy of the prices fixed by middlemen, are now able to better negotiate, quite like their counterparts in Africa. This generation of users is focused not so much on the value-added services but on the low cost of the handsets and the ability to prepay for airtime, which does not always require a credit history or even permanent residence. When they see a new mobile phone, these users ask whether it supports SMS or 'texting' and prepaid cards.

Globally in less than ten years, and in many countries such as India in less than five, the debate over whether mobile phones are a necessity or a luxury was settled in favour of the former without much argument. From downloading ring tones to music, gambling to conducting financial and non-financial transactions, and from sending short messages to video mails, mobile phones are now at the centre of life for half of humanity. This demographic is so overpowering that it carries with itself change whose extent very few people have begun to grasp. It is giving birth to a whole new set of values and attitudes that can potentially alter forever the way humans live and interact with one another. At different levels, it impacts the way people dress, talk, relate and transact. It also globalizes and personalizes economies far beyond what we have seen so far. It carries with it a million seeds for a million revolutions.

What is exciting is that unlike past technological breakthroughs and revolutions over the millennia, which spread gradually, unevenly, and depended on economic levels of different societies, the mobile telephony revolution is different because it is at once global and local, cutting across all strata of society. If people living thousands of miles apart can fathom the same audio, video, and transactional experience in real time, the lines between global and local have indeed blurred, and the world has truly become flat. Aiding all this is the international roaming feature that mobile phone operators offer as well as the ability to retain one's phone number anywhere in the world.

In the future, while content offered on the mobile phone would be of the essence and is likely to be fashioned and influenced by regional tastes, cultures, languages and so on, one common underlying reality will be that everyone with a mobile phone will be able to decide for themselves what they want to see, hear, buy and sell, irrespective of their geographic specificity.

The spread of mobile phones, and the new business models this has created, has caught the attention of many major corporations around the world. Although many of them have not quite understood the big picture and how or when it is going to unfold, corporate leaders have begun to recognize possibilities of convergence and economies of scale between sectors of business which they, till recently, believed could never come together. Telecom companies, banks and merchants, traditionally considered distinct and exclusive entities in terms of their business segments, now confront the real challenges of convergence among them brought about by mobile technology.

It is interesting that the extensive disruptive nature of mobile technology has not been fully understood by various stakeholders – both within the industry verticals or related regulatory regimes. While in the past couple of years some of them have begun to understand how mobile telephony will eventually alter major delivery and business models, the larger community has remained broadly uninformed.

Having been involved in pioneering some of the mobile phone-based applications from the early 1990s, we have been tracking the evolution of mobile telephony and how it is creating sectored changes. The first and the most obvious sector in question is that of telecom companies. From fixed-line phones to mobile phones, telecom companies have had to transform themselves in a very fundamental way. Mobility that comes with cell phones, and advances in technology, including larger displays and more computing power, have opened up all kinds of possibilities for content and service providers. A second seemingly unlikely sector to be greatly impacted by the spread of mobile telephony is the banking industry, where the ability to conduct transactions from anywhere and at any time inherently lends itself to real- time monetary settlements. In fact, the main theme of this book is how the world of banking and money will change in the face of the march of mobile phones.

We spend considerable attention on how the concept and subsequent application of money will undergo unexpected, and, in many ways, unheralded changes. A third and directly related area of interest is how retailers or merchants will restructure their business models to take advantage of the technology, not only to save costs but also to generate additional revenues through recurring sales and new services. At the risk of stating the obvious, there is absolutely no value in loading a mobile phone with money, without having the ability to spend it at a retail or merchant location, with some tangible benefit to the consumer. Hence the march of mobile money intrinsically brings together telecom companies, banks and merchants in an unprecedented manner to not only create a compelling value proposition for the user but also the various stakeholders.

Inevitably, all this would lead to a substantial overlapping of roles and territories among telecom companies, banks and merchants. Of course, this overlap will not be free from tensions and conflicts because eventually it would become a question of who acquires the customer and who influences or controls how much of the consumer's lifestyle.

We already see lifestyle management as the new battleground among these three main stakeholders.

Telecom companies have begun to see themselves as a lifestyle management pipe through which everything will flow to the end user; banks have begun to fashion themselves as a lifestyle management fund that will control the way people spend; while merchants will cast for themselves the role of a lifestyle management provider, influencing the flow of products and services.

This shift will influence and drive the evolution of telecom companies and communications, banks and banking, and merchants and merchandising.

In the case of telecom companies, it is no longer just about connectivity, where high mobile penetration has already commoditized voice and data, but the emphasis is on delivering personalized and secure services. Hence with growing opportunities will come higher pressure to increase average revenue per user (ARPU) and differentiation.

For banks, it will no longer be about just deposits and lending for the local community but about the convergence of various financial products and services. However, this impressive growth potential will come attached with higher complexities in managing risk.

Merchants will have to focus not just on goods but on goods bundled with services. Although globalization will bring more opportunities, it will also bring a great requirement for flexibility in customizing and personalizing products and services to address local markets, leveraging a global supply chain. This in turn would mean having to create new delivery and business models, increasing the pressure for creating customer loyalty and profitability.

One striking illustration of the transformation of the kind that we talk about in this book comes in the form of NTT DOCOMO, currently the dominant telecom company or wireless service provider in Japan.

iMODE & BEYOND

In February of 1999, NTT DOCOMO, the largest mobile operator in Japan, did something seminal. It created iMode, a mobile Internet access system, a development fraught with revolutionary potential. Helming iMode was Takeshi Natsuno, a boyish graduate of Wharton Business School. Natsuno's philosophy was simple yet radical. In a July 2001 profile by *Business Week*, Natsuno said something that most other telecom companies were not inclined to do: 'To become profitable ourselves, we have to motivate and enrich the content providers.'

iMode was perhaps the first major example of a path-breaking departure from mobile phones being just carriers of voice. This was driven by not only an innovative technology platform but also an equally innovative business model built to attract a high number of content and application developers. Being able to access content on mobile phones was a revolutionary step, and iMode turned out to be one of the biggest success stories in Japan in recent times. While the original NTT remained pretty much an old-fashioned legacy phone company for the first decades of its existence, DOCOMO had suddenly made a 90-degree turn. iMode opened up possibilities for mobile phones to be far more than just telephones.

Once the company had a handle on data services through iMode, it took the next important step of turning the mobile phone into an instrument of conducting transactions. The idea was to convert mobile phones into mobile wallets. Rather than restricting it to transactions through the iMode platform, it also thought about conducting them in the physical world, where the majority of transactions still take place. The trajectory of NTT – from a legacy phone company to mobile phone service provider to an entity that offered the ability to conduct transactions in real and virtual worlds – was a classic example of the transformation of roles and blurring of territories. And the company's evolution did not stop here.

According to NTT's official corporate history, 'Over time NTT DOCOMO has realized (that) in order to enable physical world transactions, they must establish strong relationship with risk management-type companies. This has driven strategic investments with banks and merchants.'

This strategy brought about yet another revolutionary change in April 2005, when the company acquired a 34 per cent stake in Sumitomo Mitsui Banking Corporation to forge an alliance to introduce mobile wallets. This decision propelled NTT DOCOMO into a whole new world of finance. So now the transition travelled through legacy phones to mobile phones to data services to financial risk management and banking. In March 2006, the company, along with UC Card Co and Mizuho Bank, announced an alliance to promote DOCOMO's iD brand card business, among other things. Some three weeks later, it announced an alliance with Lawson, a chain of convenience stores under which customers who had DOCOMO's Osaifu-Keitai phones could use them as wallets in the real-world environment of Lawson stores.

As much as we are certain that further evolution of NTT DOCOMO from a legacy telecom company to New Age lifestyle service provider will continue, DOCOMO's history, especially in the past decade, presents a glaring case study of how telecommunication companies today are in many ways being forced to cross over to the banking and retail industries, owing primarily to the advent of mobile telephony.

2

Evolution of Telecom Companies

On 10 March 1876, Alexander Graham Bell picked up his crude prototype telephone, consisting of a wooden stand and a funnel, and made the first call in human history. 'Mr Watson, come here, I want you,' were Bell's first words to his assistant. In some ways, his less than dramatic words, which heralded one of the greatest inventions, seem fitting 132 years later, as voice will no longer remain the main feature of the telephone in the future.

The history of communication is intrinsic to human history as people have for millennia had the urge to reach out and connect with what is beyond them. From the jungle drums of Africa to smoke signals to pigeons to mirrors to horse-mounted messengers, humans have tried everything to get their message across.

Legend has it that in 490 BC, the town of Marathon, on the coast of the Aegean Sea, witnessed a brutal battle between a contingent of the Greek army and Persian soldiers. After the Greeks defeated the Persians, it was important that a communication be sent to Athens. A messenger was sent to travel some 40 kilometres on foot with the message of victory. As he reached the streets of Athens he was exhausted but elated. 'Be glad, we are the winners,' he said, even as he collapsed and later died. From that time till the actual telephone came into existence, some 2300 years had passed.

There is some record in Homer's epic *Iliad* in 1200 BC about fire signals having been used. Carrier pigeons were extensively used between 700 BC and 300 AD. Jumping some 1200 years, in 1588, the arrival of the Spanish Armada was announced by fire signals. All of these were early examples of attempts at telecommunication.

There is some speculation about whether the invention of the telephone instrument was presaged by Francis Bacon in 1627, when he spoke of transmitting voice over a long speaking tube. Although that sounds intriguing, Bacon could not have had anything resembling Bell's phone in mind because the underlying electrical principles did not come into existence until the early 1800s. According to Tom Farley's Telephone History Series (http://www.privateline.com/TelephoneHistory/History1.htm), 'Who in the fifteenth century might have imagined a pay phone on the street corner or a fax machine on their desk? You didn't have then an easily visualized goal among people, like powered flight, resulting in one inventor after another working through the years to realize a common goal. Telephone development instead was a series of often disconnected events, mostly electrical, some accidental, that made the telephone possible.'

By 1831, Michael Faraday had published his findings on induction and effectively set the stage for future inventors to build on that. According to Farley and others, it wasn't until 1854 that Charles Bourseul suggested transmitting speech electrically. In fact, this Brussels-born engineer had already experimented with electrical transmission of voice. Some two decades later, Bell made the first phone call.

In between that period, the invention of telegraphy in 1838 by Samuel Finley Breese Morse promised to run away with the honour of the most important breakthrough in communications. Telegraphy gained rapid ground in the three decades after its invention. In 1866, a good decade before Bell's historic phone call, a transatlantic cable connecting America and Europe by telegraph was in place.

The evolution of basic voice telephony is a great example of how various technologies had to converge to deliver a complete communication solution. For instance, the invention of the microphone by Elisha Gray (1835-1901), the invention of the alternating current power system by Nikola Telsa (1856-1943), and the discovery of electromagnetic waves by Friedrich Hertz all fed into the early development of telecommunications.

The evolution of telecom companies as we know them today really began with British Telecommunications (now BT), the world's oldest telecommunications company, which had its origin in the era of telegraphy and began as the Electric Telegraph Company in 1846. Nearly three decades later, AT&T, which was founded by Bell, emerged in the US. 'During the nineteenth century, AT&T became the parent company of the Bell System, the American telephone monopoly. The Bell System provided what was by all accounts the best telephone service in the world. The system was broken up into eight companies in 1984 by agreement between AT&T and the US Department of Justice,' according to AT&T's corporate history.

Over the last 160 years, telecom companies such as BT and AT&T have largely evolved as providers of telecommunication infrastructure, focusing mainly on voice transmission. With the advent of the Internet came the requirement of moving large amounts of data and eventually images, forcing these providers to continuously upgrade and enhance their networks. As economies in North America and

Western Europe rapidly grew after the Second World War, the term 'dispensable-income' came into vogue, increasing the emphasis on entertainment and value addition as opposed to just basic necessities. Consequently, telecommunication providers started looking at value-added services over just basic telephony, and what initially was triggered by cable providers has now led to convergence of not only different infrastructure networks but also applications ranging from basic voice-calling to pay-on-demand movies to enterprise VPNs to wireless video-telephony.

A typical telephone network consists of customer premise equipments such as telephones, fax, modems, computers, etc. The transmission systems consist of wires, cables, fibre, satellites, and associated electronic and switching systems to switch and route calls. The early telecom network started with patch chords and manual operators to connect the called party to the calling party. Then came mechanical relays, analogue electronic switching, and finally digital networks, where analogue voice was converted to digital bits and bytes with 1s and 0s.

The digital era brought in quality of voice that was independent of distance. There were substantial changes to the features and functionalities of the telecom network, with special software programmes for flexibility, routing, billing, management, etc. However, the telephone instrument and assigned number remained allocated to a fixed location like home or office.

With the advent of wireless networks, assigned numbers acquired unprecedented mobility, enabling the user to take the telephone instrument anywhere-anytime outside the wired world. This was made possible by dividing physical space into small cells of wireless connectivity, where wireless mobile phone signals could be connected to a base unit, which in turn could be connected to the landline network or another base unit to communicate with the rest of the wired or wireless world. Each base unit normally has the ability to connect a predetermined number of mobile phones through wireless means in an assigned frequency band. Just as wired line systems require physical space to lay wires and cables to connect, mobile phones require spectrum, which is normally auctioned by governments, to connect as airway assets.

Like with all great technologies, the average user of mobile technology is neither aware of, nor should be concerned with, what goes into making this complex technology work. A typical mobile phone for its user consists of a face plate, a keypad, a display screen, and various applications. For the better part of mobile telephony's history, the display screen has been rather small, residing on a standard face plate. The applications offered by mobile phones have been confined to voice and some level of data transmission. It is only in the last three to five years that mobile phones have begun to acquire much larger display screens, greater processing power and applications beyond just voice transmission. For quite some time, the difference between mobile phones and fixed line phones was that the former allowed mobility and was not tied down to a location. Beyond mobility, which was of course a greater breakthrough, both mobile phones and fixed line phones served pretty much the same functions.

During the early 1980s, even this mobility was restricted within national boundaries. As much as the US led early developments in wireless communications, initially for its military and eventually for civilian purposes, analogue cellular telephone systems grew rapidly in Europe, including Scandinavia, the UK, France and Germany. These countries had their own equipment and transmission standards. The system in one country was incompatible with the rest in terms of equipment and operation. This lack of uniform standards stifled the growth of analogue cellular telephone systems. In 1982, the Conference of European Posts and Telegraphs (CEPT) formed a study group called the Groupe Spécial Mobile (GSM) to study and develop a pan-European public land mobile system. The main objectives of the study were good subjective speech quality, low terminal and service cost, support for international roaming, ability to support handheld terminals, support for a range of new services and compatibility. After GSM specifications were published in 1990, commercial service began in mid-1991. In the following two years there were thirty-six GSM networks operating in twenty-two countries.

While GSM grew as a widely accepted standard in mobile telephony, an inevitable rival was round the corner in the form of CDMA, short for Code-Division Multiple Access. Unlike GSM, CDMA does not assign a specific frequency to each user. Instead, every channel uses the full available spectrum. CDMA's origins were in the military, where during the Second World War, England and her allies transmitted cryptic messages over several frequencies to thwart German attempts at jamming transmissions. Supporters of GSM and CDMA both argue that their respective technologies provide better capacity for voice and data communication, leading to better signal-to-noise ratios or quality, availability and efficiency, which consequently affect not only user adoption but also deployment costs and regulatory requirements.

GSM phones are characterized by the presence of the SIM or subscriber identity module, where the SIM card stores the subscriber's identity on the network, enabling the user to switch handsets without changing the number as long as the same SIM card is used. Many CDMA standards do not include a card, where the service is linked to a unique identifier on the handset.

Eventually, much of Asia, Africa, Middle East and Latin America adopted GSM, with the US following several different standards. Today, three quarters of all mobile subscribers worldwide use GSM, while the others use

26

CDMA-based networks. In the early days, one of the key factors contributing to the growth of GSM was its ability to seamlessly roam across multiple regions.

One of the promises of the third and fourth generation telecommunication networks is true standardization, which will enable seamless connectivity, international roaming, and the development of a global community of service providers and application developers. Not thwarted by incompatible networks and handsets, they will be better able to realize economies of scale by delivering several localized services over a single global platform.

All communications need frequencies to transmit information. As mobile telephony grew in the 1990s, pressure on frequency allocation also increased. Since 1994 the Federal Communications Commission (FCC) in the US, as well as its counterparts in other countries, have conducted auctions in order to assign spectrum to telecommunication providers. Hundreds of billions of dollars have been spent by mobile phone operators in acquiring specific and unique frequencies on which to transmit their voice and data. The first auction of airwaves, or a slice of the electromagnetic spectrum, was carried out in July 1994 at Omni Shoreham Hotel in Washington DC. It generated $617 million for just ten small licenses. The next auction in December of that year raised more than $7 billion. This was considered a record for the sale of public goods in America. *The New York Times* called it 'the greatest auction ever'. Auctioning spectrum is now a standard method throughout the world.

The wireless world has moved from 2G to 2.5G to 3G quickly in the last decade. Now even 4G is on the horizon. The need to upgrade is based on the ever increasing demand for data services. As more and more mobile customers begin to exchange SMS, MMS, pictures, videos and other services that require more and more bandwidth, the networks need to be upgraded simultaneously to handle the ever increasing traffic. It is well known in the industry that the rise of Apple iPhone has created severe pressures on AT&T network for data handling. 3G and 4G networks facilitate high speed data transmissions on the network and between devices.

The 3G spectrum auction in India in 2010 reaffirmed yet again how economically decisive spectrum is to nation-building. The Indian network is predominantly driven by voice traffic. Unfortunately, 3G auctions were delayed in India for several years because of the fact that the defence forces were using some part of the band and needed to vacate it to facilitate commercialization. Before vacating, defence had to be assured of alternative arrangement and smooth transition to carry their existing data traffic from wireless 3G-related band to other suitable, preferably fixed line, media.

The debate between defence, wireless advisers, the Department of Telecom, the Telecom Regulatory Authority of India and other agencies took unduly long. At one time, there were serious discussions to turn this decision over to a group of ministers.

Fortunately, professional wisdom prevailed and an understanding was achieved to free up the spectrum to help commercialize through 3G auctions.

In the end, it turned out to be a smooth affair with the auctions generating a staggering Rs 1,06,000 crore (over $20 billion) for the government, a resource that could be used to transform the lives of hundreds of millions of people.

As mobile telephony has become more firmly entrenched as a tool for communication, it has created three distinct stakeholders – telecom companies, which provide the networks and services; device and equipment manufacturers, which provide the phone instruments and infrastructure; and consumers, who use what the other two provide. In order for the whole industry to grow, all three stakeholders have a crucial role to play.

Similarly, in the past few years, three major players – telecom companies and cable and content providers – have moved to a common ground to offer services that were not considered typical of them traditionally. The result of this shift has been manifest, for instance, in cable operators emerging from being providers of cable TV content to becoming providers of broadband services, and eventually, Voice-over Internet Protocol. Telecom companies, on the

SPECTRUM ALLOCATION

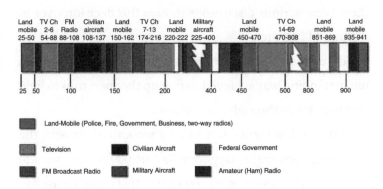

| Land mobile 25-50 | TV Ch 2-6 54-88 | FM Radio 88-108 | Civilian aircraft 108-137 | Land mobile 150-162 | TV Ch 7-13 174-216 | Land mobile 220-222 | Military aircraft 225-400 | Land mobile 450-470 | TV Ch 14-69 470-808 | Land mobile 851-869 | Land mobile 935-941 |

25 50   100   150   200   400 450   500 800   900

- Land-Mobile (Police, Fire, Government, Business, two-way radios)

- Television
- FM Broadcast Radio

- Civilian Aircraft
- Military Aircraft

- Federal Government
- Amateur (Ham) Radio

GLOBAL MOBILE TELEPHONE STATISTICS

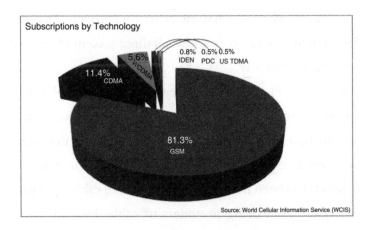

Subscriptions by Technology

0.8% IDEN   0.5% PDC   0.5% US TDMA

5.6% WCDMA

11.4% CDMA

81.3% GSM

Source: World Cellular Information Service (WCIS)

other hand, have moved from being providers of voice to high-speed Internet/Data over DSL, or Digital Subscriber Line, and various value-added services. Such shifts are not limited to just these three specific names but represent an overall trend, where hitherto distinct telecom entities are refashioning their roles.

Since mobile telephony has become the mainstay of the global telecommunication business, much more so than fixed lines, it is the latest frontier for convergence. Unlike fixed-line phones, which have remained largely frozen in their utility, mobile phones have quickly redefined their roles as purveyors of data beyond just voice, and have become an extension of an individual's identity.

The very definition of telephone is limited by its Greek origin. 'Tele' means 'far' or 'at some distance' and 'phone' means 'voice', the two words together meaning 'carrying voice to a distance'. That definition is outdated because mobile communication is anything but just voice communication. With applications such as video phones, where audio and video streaming reside on mobile phones, perhaps there is a need for a whole new nomenclature for modern communication.

Beyond this broad convergence of roles and their redefinition, for a brief period in the 1990s, there was also a great buzz about the fixed-mobile convergence (FMC). It was seen as the ultimate technological merger, where the difference between fixed-line phones and mobile phones would be practically erased in terms of the services they offered. It was argued that value-added features, such as caller ID, call waiting and voicemail, which fixed-line operators offered, would be given by mobile phone operators. Simultaneously, it was predicted that fixed-line phones would acquire worldwide mobility with number portability. All this would happen under a single umbrella, a single bill, and a single customer service. Of course, some of those predictions did come true, but the larger vision of FMC has remained unfulfilled.

Beyond convergence of different networks, there have also been several merger attempts between providers of equipment and infrastructure with content providers. In an age where content and applications rule, it did not take long for infrastructure providers with significant assets and reach to notice the value addition created by content developers and service providers. While many of these mergers have yet to prove successful, the trend has been established and will definitely continue.

One example of such conversence is British Telecom, whose history and current strategies lead one to believe that this once written-off archaic infrastructure provider may actually teach some of the new entrants a valuable lesson or two in the art of customer acquisition and retention.

British Telecom (BT)

As the world's oldest telecom company (established in 1846), British Telecom or BT began as the Electric Telegraph Company in the mid-nineteenth century along with other telecom companies, which, along the way, amalgamated or were taken over or simply collapsed. It was finally transferred to state control under the post office. In 1982, it was privatized as British Telecom.

That one action freed up British Telecom to pursue its own ventures, including manufacturing of its own apparatus. The decade of the 1980s saw a lot of churning within the British Telecom world. In 1991, a government white paper ended the duopoly between British Telecom and Mercury Communications. This opened up competition as it allowed independent retailers to tap into excess telecom capacity and resell it at rates of their choice.

That same year British Telecom changed its name to BT and carried out major corporate restructuring. The new thinking led to something dramatic. In June 1994, BT and MCI Communication Corporation, then the second largest long-distance service provider in the US, together launched Concert Communications for multinational customers. In November 1996, the two companies announced their decision to merge to create a global company called Concert PLC. BT acquired a 20 per cent stake in MCI but that bid was upstaged in October 1997, when US carrier WorldCom acquired a rival stake. Eventually BT decided to sell its stake to WorldCom for $7 billion.

In 2004, BT embarked on Consult21, 'an industry consultation for BT's twenty-first century network (21CN) programme.' It has been described as the world's 'most ambitious and radical next-generation network transformation.' The programme would transform the UK's communication infrastructure by 2010, using Internet protocol technology, and enable convergence for multimedia communication from any device such as a mobile phone, PC, PDA, or home phone. This was considered radical for an old, traditional phone company. It was changing itself from a traditional telecom company to 'a leading provider of converged networked services'.

For close to twenty years, starting in the 1980s, BT and Vodafone were the most talked about telecom companies in Europe. BT's strategy to straddle the whole gamut of fixed-line telephony and being a provider of converged networked services was being viewed with a great deal of skepticism as opposed to Vodafone's plan to grow globally purely on the basis of wireless mobile telephony. Many industry experts believed Vodafone's was the way to go. Industry analysts thought Vodafone's choice of wireless over copper wires made eminent sense. The performance of the company seemed to support that analysis as it became the largest mobile company in the world in terms of revenue, enjoying 170 million subscribers in twenty-five countries.

But more recently, things have started turning as BT has consolidated itself. For a while, BT did attempt to go the Vodafone way through its mobile division O2. But by November 2004, it had realized that perhaps that was not the strategy to pursue.

The journey of telecom companies from being carriers of voice for over a century, and more recently data, towards becoming a lifestyle management pipe, is quite interesting. With voice becoming commoditized and with the rapid growth of broadband, telecom companies have begun to recognize that in their quest to increase their ARPU and differentiation against competitors, they can no longer remain providers of just voice services. We are fast approaching a phase of evolution in telecommunications where voice will become not just incidental but improbably cheap, if not free altogether.

3

Evolution of Banks

According to *A History of Money from Ancient Times to the Present Day* by Glyn Davies (Cardiff: University of Wales Press, 1996), after the domestication of cattle and cultivation of crops, between 9000 BC and 6000 BC livestock and grain emerged as forms of money. Livestock, in fact, preceded crops as a form of currency.

For about 3,000 to 6,000 years, in various societies across Asia and Africa, people's conception of money differed from modern times only in its form, but the underlying principle, that you have to spend something to acquire something else, has been understood for a long time. That basic definition of money has not changed for over 11,000 years of recorded history.

It was around 3000 BC that writing was invented in Mesopotamia, modern-day Iraq. With that the idea of money underwent a fundamental shift. A millennium or so later, banking was invented in Mesopotamia. According to Davies, 'Banking originates in Babylonia out of the activities of temples and palaces, which provided safe places for the storage of valuables. Initially deposits of grain are accepted and later other goods, including cattle, agricultural implements, and precious metals.'

A few centuries later, the rulers in Babylon began guaranteeing weight and purity of silver ingots in what was perhaps the first example of the state promise to back a form of currency. By 1750 BC, Hammurabi of Babylon had laid down a code that included, among other things, laws governing banking.

It was another five centuries before people in China began using what was probably the first example of an actual currency in the form of cowrie shells. Although these shells were used in other societies, in China they seemed to gain rapid acceptance. There was a gap of another four-odd centuries before coins were minted as a form of formal currency in 687 BC in Lydia, according to Greek historian Herodotus.

Connected with the evolution of money and currency is the growth of banking. In its early days, and pretty much throughout its history, banking was a localized and even intimate activity. Those who had the strongboxes and those who had strong moral fibre emerged as the custodians of people's money and other forms of wealth. Banking was usually the business of moneylenders who, despite being despised, were still a necessity, or others who inspired trust and had access to capital as well as secure physical infrastructure such as strongboxes.

From 687 BC to the present, money has taken several avatars but essentially remained the same in that it has been used as a benchmark to measure success, both for individuals and society, and therefore a yardstick to also measure the social standing and political soundness of nations and empires.

The role of money in people's lives in medieval times as well as modern times has been simple yet profound. Any exchange of goods and services has always been accompanied by some form of payment. That payment could be explicit, such as exchanging two cows for bags of wheat in Babylon, or swiping a credit card to buy a pair of shoes in New York or finalizing an armament contract in exchange for a reciprocal amount in foreign direct investment. Or it could be something implicit, such as you picking up someone from the airport in the middle of the night and later getting treated to a lunch as a thank-you gesture. There is always some hidden or not-so-hidden financial or non-financial transaction involved.

In order to legitimize such transactions, physical currency was invented, first in the form of gold, silver and copper

coins, and then in the form of promissory notes and eventually, currency bills. In many ways, the invention of portable currency, be it coins or notes, was a direct result of people's demand for convenience. As societies progressed, populations grew and communications expanded, it became harder to carry livestock or crops as a form of currency. Right up to the dawn of the twentieth century, the formal system of money more or less remained what it had been when it was first introduced in China as cowrie shells.

The first major evolution beyond currency, specifically in terms of 'cash-replacement' instruments, came in the form of bank-issued paper cheques. Cheques as an instrument of payment have been in existence since the very early part of the twentieth century. Cheques in pre-computerization days used to take weeks to clear among various banks because they had to be physically verified. Quite obviously, they could be issued only if one had enough money in one's account to cover a particular amount. Even though bounced cheques have been around as long as the system of cheques itself, the principle is that bank account holders would issue cheques only when they had sufficient funds to do so. In more recent times, with the advent of the Internet as a growing channel for both consumer-to-business (or C2B) electronic payments as well as business-to-business (or B2B) electronic payments, the use of paper cheques has started to fall though it still continues to be one of the popular forms of cash-alternative payment methods, especially in the US.

Paper cheques came into vogue primarily owing to convenience – that is, convenience to the consumer, which in turn led to retailers or merchants accepting paper cheques as a form of payment. Hence it is safe to state that paper cheques introduced the concepts of 'issuance', 'merchant acceptance', 'acquisition', 'settlement' and 'risk'. All five terms have profound significance as we examine the further evolution of money and, specifically, its digitization over the years.

With paper cheques came the need for issuance, acquisition and settlement; that is, someone had to issue the cheques to the consumer, someone had to acquire the cheques from the merchants, and someone had to settle them between the entity that issued the cheque and the one that was owed a payment. Acceptance of cheques at a retail location was based on the ability of the retailer to settle cheques, the amount that the retailer was willing to accept risk for, and the cost or settlement fees associated with the transaction. Though the underlying principle, as stated before, was that one issued a cheque only for an amount that was available in the bank, this was not always the case. Hence over and above issuance, acquisition, and settlement, a separate industry has evolved over the years around the business of managing risk associated with cheques, providing insurance for this risk to merchants, and collection of bad cheques. One of the more significant developments related to paper cheques in the US in recent years has been the Cheque 21 Act or 21st Century Cheque Clearing Act, geared towards increasing efficiencies related to collection and returns as opposed to mere physical transportation of paper cheques.

Despite its popularity, the fact remains that writing cheques is an expensive and time consuming process that adds to overall costs for everyone, not to mention the environmental costs of using so much paper. From printing hundreds of millions of cheque books, to writing and mailing them, opening and sorting envelops, updating systems and settling between banks, it all adds up to significant costs without many of us realizing it. It involves a large number of people doing a large number of chores every day, and in some cases there are dedicated factories set up just to process paper cheque-based payments. These overheads or costs for supporting cheques have to be recovered and are often built into the cost of goods or services offered by merchants, effectively coming from the consumer.

In some ways, by establishing scalable methodologies and platforms for issuance, (merchant) acceptance, acquisition, settlement, and risk for cash-alternative products, paper cheques paved the way for a whole new system of payment, namely credit cards, which would fundamentally alter the socioeconomics of not just America but eventually the rest of the world.

In the early decades of the twentieth century, gasoline companies and stores in America began issuing credit cards that were recognized within their own system. The idea was aimed at making it convenient for their customers to spend. Rather than carrying cash or paper cheque books, people began carrying these individual cards. It was in the 1950s that Diner's Club first introduced a credit card that could be used more widely and across market segments. This was followed by banks issuing their own cards but due to the fragmentation in the banking world, a card that could be used nationwide was hard to come by. As a result, banks got together and started two main cooperative ventures to create the necessary standardization across the banking and retail industries, as well as processing payments. These two ventures eventually evolved into MasterCard and Visa.

As a first step, these two cooperatives sent out a large number of unsolicited invitations to a large number of people, though the creditworthiness of many of them was not established. In the early days of credit cards, banks lost a lot of money because of unpaid bills, a situation that continues till today. Outside of MasterCard and Visa, American Express, which pioneered traveller's cheques, and Discover also offer credit cards, primarily differentiating on value-added services over points of acceptance. Unlike MasterCard and Visa, which started operating through their member banks, American Express and Discover are banks themselves, offering various financial services in addition to credit cards. More recently, with the listing of MasterCard and Visa on the public markets, the industry expects both entities to take radically different courses in the future, leveraging their strong brands, expertise in risk management, and banking and merchant relationships to potentially drive down transaction costs and deliver value-added services, especially through emerging channels such as mobile phones, directly to the consumers.

Over the years, large retailers have continued to offer their 'closed-loop' credit cards, once again differentiating on value-added services, such as rewards, coupons and promotions, but effectively using these store cards to generate additional revenue through interest payments on what effectively become small loans. Aside from launching closed-loop store-branded credit cards, large retailers have also launched another lucrative cash-replacement instrument in the form of stored-value cards. Stored-value cards and/or gift cards have become immensely popular with consumers from a convenience standpoint, and have generated additional revenue streams for merchants and their processors through various processing fees and 'float', or the interest collected over deposits for goods that have not yet been delivered. Take, for example, stored-value cards of major store chains such as Gap or Banana Republic. If there are five million people with stored-value cards worth $20 each, it means that already $100 million is taken out of traditional banking. While there are no official estimates available, the money riding on stored-value cards alone could amount to several billion dollars. This is equally true of frequent flyer cards, which also represent money in some form. There are already strategies in place in Japan, for instance, where airline miles can be converted into real cash to buy unrelated goods and services.

So while banks scramble to create and consolidate a lifestyle management fund, there is growing pressure on them from non-banking players, who are also getting more deeply involved in money management. Money is becoming more diverse and widely dispersed and, as a result, going out of the sole control of a particular industry. Another interesting example is the amount people spend on road toll. For instance, in Chicago city, some 3 million people use the toll-ways. The way it works is that people pay an advance monthly fee of up to $40. For the toll authorities, this means they have at least $120 million in the bank. Although money is drawn from this account every time a toll user passes through a toll booth, at any given time there is still a lot of unused cash that the toll authorities can leverage. Beyond the unused cash, the bigger issue is about the float, or the interest generated on such large stored-value amounts. Typically, such interest is not passed on to the consumer but taken by the entity sitting on these amounts. The entire interest on the stored-value amount works out to a sizeable sum that comes to such entities completely free.

Twenty years ago, if someone had a thousand dollars, chances were that the entire amount would be committed to a bank account as a deposit. That is no longer the case now. Out of a thousand dollars, after committing on other avenues such as stored-value cards and toll, a customer will probably keep 500 to 600 dollars in the bank. That is a net loss to the banks. Hence the next time you pick up a stored-value card or a gift card, think of it as an advance payment to the merchant for goods or services not yet collected!

However, it was not enough to have a large number of people subscribe to cards that could be processed nationwide unless there were enough merchants who would actually accept those cards as a form of payment and offer goods and services in return. That led to the creation of a network of merchants who joined either of the two credit card issuers or both. These merchants were part of American Express, Discover, MasterCard, Visa and other payment systems, including closed-loop systems as described earlier, which would allow customers to walk into a store without any cash in hand, and often without enough money in their own bank accounts, to make purchases using what were essentially short-term loans extended to them. The buy-now-pay-later mantra began catching up rapidly among America's middle class as they recognized the obvious benefits of not having money and yet being able to spend it because a third party was willing to facilitate their aspirations. It is a different story that many of them did not recognize the inherent dangers of spending money without really having it.

Ranging from an average consumer in the US, who has five credit cards with upwards of $4,000 revolving balance or loan per card, or a college student effectively using credit cards to pay through graduation, or a small business getting a special credit card as an extension of the company's line of credit, all of these in some way directly or indirectly impact the much-cited fiscal benchmark of consumer confidence, which in turn influences the capital markets, interest rates, exchange rates and, eventually, the flow of commerce and money throughout the world.

The US banks and financial institutions have been exporting credit cards overseas, notably in Asia, where consumers have typically avoided borrowing so freely. NTT DOCOMO, which was profiled earlier, tried to jumpstart the Japanese economy by increasing credit card usage – it embedded them in cell phones. China and India, which are cited as the future markets for retail banking, have also started seeing strong growth in the number of credit cards in recent years.

The logical next step to credit cards, which lent people money they did not have and often could not earn and hence made them run up huge debts, was debit cards. They look, feel and operate precisely like credit cards, except instead of short-term loans, the funds are drawn from your bank account the moment you spend it.

With the growing number of credit cards, and increasing complexities in managing the associated risk and fraud, several markets around the world started looking at a more localized authentication technology, which did not need real-time authorization from a remote system to complete a transaction at a point of sale. Given the popularity of the plastic card metaphor, the natural evolution was to replace or augment the static magnetic stripe on the plastic card (credit or debit) with a smart chip that essentially required a PIN or password to be entered by the consumer at the point of sale. The mechanism of authenticating the PIN was tamper-proof, effectively reducing fraud, and at the same time not requiring real-time authorization from a remote settlement system to process the transaction. Chip cards, or smart cards as they are popularly referred to, have become popular in some regions and failed to take off in others. Given that these cards require the installation of new hardware at the point of sale, merchants have resisted paying for this infrastructure upgrade in markets where the current real-time settlement systems are adequate and the incremental advantages of reducing fraud do not outweigh the cost of upgrading the existing point of sale terminals and supporting infrastructure. The promise of smart cards delivering other value-added services has also not quite materialized, and in some ways may be eclipsed by the advent of mobile phones as a more robust and ubiquitous channel for not only reducing the risk associated with payments but also delivering more personalized and localized value-added services.

The dramatic growth of credit card and debit card users around the world, whose number easily runs into hundreds of millions, has compelled banks and other credit card issuers to invest in creating a global payment infrastructure, which includes equipment such as card readers and settlement networks, as well as in human resources required to market, operate, process and support hundreds of billions of dollars' worth of transactions.

As computers became smarter and more powerful in the 1970s, banks began to explore possibilities of not just computerizing their records but also better facilities for their customers. Bank computerization began with the back office, where records of transactions were stored on ledgers that were maintained manually. A vast amount of financial data related to deposits, withdrawals, loans, etc. had to be computerized before banks could think of bringing the benefits of computer technology directly to their customers. In a sense, the back office computerization was aimed more at making record-keeping easier for banks themselves, through it was also of consequence for the customers.

48

Then began the computerization of the front office. What that meant was that a customer could walk up to a teller and obtain information much more quickly via the teller's computer, unlike in the past, when a bank clerk would actually open the ledger and manually check entries. Those entries had to be reflected in the customer's individual pass books as well. This was a very tedious process, vulnerable to serious entry inaccuracies. The front end computerization made banking a much easier process. With computerization also came electronic transfers among different banks. Processing of millions of cheque transactions daily, which were till the 1970s done through a tedious manual process, became easier with faster computers and networks interconnecting different banks.

After nearly twenty years of computerization both at the back and front ends of banking, in the early 1990s, banks pushed customer experience a step forward. With automation and increasing costs associated with delivery of services that required trained and dedicated human resources, banks started deploying Auto Teller Machines (ATM), which (for the large part) could be set up at a street corner and which offered convenience in terms of proximity and timing, since these could be accessed any time of day and night. Initially, banks had their own closed-loop ATM networks. Gradually, interoperability between different ATM networks evolved, so that today, for a fee, one can use

a debit card or credit card issued by one bank to withdraw cash from an ATM operated by another, and also effectively utilize bank-issued cards as instruments of foreign exchange by using them to withdraw cash from an ATM in the local currency.

With the emergence of the Internet as a global pathway for moving data and connecting consumers to businesses, businesses to businesses, businesses to governments, and governments to consumers, it was only natural that it would a play a central role in the movement of funds amongst all these entities – that is, consumers, businesses and government. For banks and the settlement industry at large, the Internet provided the backbone to offer direct banking and financial services to consumers through Internet banking, providing real-time invoicing and payment capabilities to businesses, and offering bill payment capabilities or electronic bills and payments (EBPP) to both consumers as well as to enterprise.

The Internet has also facilitated the emergence of a new breed of entities that are traditionally not banks, such as PayPal, to provide financial services directly to consumers. The Internet has taken the advantage away from financial service providers that leveraged their closed-loop network as a barrier of entry, thus levelling the playing field in many ways. The cross-border remittance business is one such example, where a new set of entities is now providing money transfer capabilities to masses across the world, and in the process reducing what would otherwise have been high and exorbitant costs. The cost savings in this instance have a considerable and direct socioeconomic effect, as the beneficiaries in most cases are blue-collar workers who typically send money back to their families.

The global payment infrastructure has grown into a behemoth of staggering proportions over the last fifty years, with thousands of big and small banks and other financial institutions and credit card companies, clearing houses, federal reserve authorities and other regulators coming into play. What began as trading two cows for bags of wheat some 11,000 years ago is now a process of incomprehensible complexity, where multiple players do multiple tasks across the globe. While all this goes on behind the scenes, there are people like you and us, hundreds of millions of them, who every minute of the 24-hour cycle are carrying out some financial transaction or the other, be it in a bank, a store, a post office, a grocer, a movie theatre or a hospital. All transactions are eventually handled by some bank or the other, and in the process they wield enormous power on our daily lives. Something which began as a very personal, even intimate, activity has now grown into a mammoth exercise carried out by banking institutions with global operations, which handle hundreds of billions of dollars every day.

When you consider the assets of the top fifty banks in the world, you realize how deeply entrenched they are in our daily lives and how globally influential they are. Their influence is felt every day, be it in people's shopping and spending habits, international exchange rates, monetary policies of countries around the world and the overall financial health of the world economy. According to the Society for Worldwide Interbank Financial Telecommunication (SWIFT), a network used by banks and other financial institutions worldwide to carry out daily transactions, some six trillion dollars get transacted every day. That amount is one-fifth of the total global economy and gives you an indication of how much is at stake in the world of money. It is natural that in an industry as powerful and as fundamental to human existence as banking, the advent of a new technology that could completely alter the way they operate could cause serious apprehensions and even resentments.

However, in the past couple of years, perceptions within the banking industry about new technologies have begun to change. The advance in computer technology and growth in mobile telephony are being viewed by major banking corporations as instruments of perpetuating their control on lifestyle management. The growing convergence between goods and services is being treated as an opportunity by banks to create and consolidate a single lifestyle management fund. If the name of the game for telecom companies is to control a lifestyle management pipe and hence shape consumer behaviour, for the banks the game is to use a lifestyle management fund to directly and indirectly influence consumer behaviour. While some major banks have begun to understand the fundamental change taking place with a bearing on the future of the industry as a whole, most either have not grasped it or have not become conscious of it yet.

For the better part of the twentieth century, when modern banking as we know it now came into being, the cost of capital was determined by many factors, including the amount of money that banks spent on creating their bricks and mortar infrastructure. When a customer goes to a branch of a major bank, he or she is struck by the opulence of furniture, interior design, carpeting, teller counters and so on. Once you add up the cost of maintaining such elaborate bricks and mortar infrastructure over a wide geography, you begin to understand the mechanics and politics of the cost of capital. The interest rates that banks charge on lending money are significantly influenced by the cost that they incur in maintaining their infrastructure and other overheads (arguably high salaries and bonuses paid regularly to their staff, especially on the investment banking side of the business, where commissions paid to the bank are not always commensurate with performance).

Mobile telephony and transaction technology together

have the potential to completely alter the banking industry worldwide. It is now possible to conduct most banking applications on a mobile phone rather than by going to a bank branch or an ATM. To that extent mobile phones are no less than mobile ATMs. While the top leadership of the banking world does understand the inevitability of this paradigm shift, it is still reluctant to accept it. Like all paradigm shifts, the trigger for this change in banking will come from a maverick who has no stake in continuing the status quo that traditional banks may like to hang on to. When there are 2 billion mobile phones with some ability to transact, is it possible or even wise to stop the change that is bound to happen?

Contrary to popular notions, the banking industry is not a monolith but has many compartments. Many banks think credit card companies may not be necessary since banks can offer all the convenience and security that credit card companies do. Credit card companies, on the other hand, are building their own portfolio of services to differentiate themselves and prove that they are indeed important. It is in line with these shifts that PayPal is now branded as a banking player even though in its original form it was not one. With this new role, however, major banks are looking at PayPal as an FSP, or financial service provider, and hence a threat.

Over the past two decades, a vast communication infrastructure has been created for any new disruptive player to ride on. New technologies will be able to leverage this existing infrastructure and create wholly new models of business. One of the most likely trends in the evolution of banks will be that using this global infrastructure, new players will be able to localize and customize their products and services. For instance, a small community bank in an African village will be able to use the global communication infrastructure to offer products and services that are specifically tailored to the very local needs of farmers, unlike what a bank in Manhattan might offer Wall Street executives. Both banks will use the same quality of infrastructure but what they offer using it would be remarkably different – microfinance for new seeds for African farmers and lower rates to trade online for Wall Street executives, for instance.

CITIBANK

While most major banks are recalibrating their strategies and role in the face of technological transformation, we would like to focus on what is being done by Citibank.

As it approaches two centuries of operations by 2012, Citibank enjoys the status of being the world's largest bank by increasingly extending smaller loans. The bank has issued 150 million credit cards, which are essentially small loans. At an average of $1,000 per credit card in spending limit, the bank has lent more than $150 billion. With that amount alone, other than what it has invested elsewhere, Citibank presents a strong example of how much influence banks wield on our daily lives. The bank's journey began in 1812, under the name City Bank of New York. By 1894 it had become the largest in the US, and three years later, it became the first major bank to establish a foreign department and begin foreign exchange trading. The bank's intentions of what it wanted to become were clear in 1902, when it expanded into Asia, Europe and India, with offices from Shanghai to Manila. By 1919 it had become the first US bank with assets of $1 billion. From that milestone to the present day, Citibank has grown into a financial juggernaut.

Although as a bank it always directly impacted a large number of people, when it entered the credit card business in 1965, it introduced the 'First National City Charge Service', popularly known as the 'Everything' card, redefining its role of merely being a deposit-withdrawal financial service provider. The significance of the 'Everything' card becomes clear to modern-day users when they discover that the card went on to become Master Charge in 1969 and eventually, today's MasterCard. It is interesting to track the transition of a modest New York bank in the early nineteenth century into today's Citibank. The period of the 1970s witnessed the evolution of the bank's holding company from The First National City Corporation to Citicorp. The decade also

marked the bank's entry into the electronic era, as it launched

Citicard Banking Centers in 1977, anchored by ATMs and the Citicard. According to the company's website, 'The 24-hour ATMs are for the first time used for more than emergency cash.' That became a major step in the direction of anytime banking that we are all so accustomed to now.

In 1985, the bank took another seminal step when it introduced Direct Access in New York, linking personal computers in homes and offices with Citibank. A year later, the bank launched touch-screen ATMs in New York City and Hong Kong, a sort of precursor to touch-screen mobile phones of today. By 1993, it had become the largest credit card and charge card issuer and servicer in the world. In 1999, Citibank launched CitiDirect Online Banking, 'the first multi-product, multi-geographic Internet banking system.'

Today, while the bank is being transformed owing to the global financial crisis, it is largely organized into different business groups, such as Global Consumer, Corporate and Investment Banking, Global Wealth Management, Citigroup Alternative Investments, and others. Between these groups the bank covers most major areas of finance, including banking services, credit cards, loans and insurance, apart from 'industry-leading' technology.

Citibank is a good example of how far banking has travelled over the last two centuries. Banking today is no longer just about deposits and lending for local communities. It is about the convergence of various services and channels into a single lifestyle management fund. Although opportunities for banks have grown exponentially, they have also brought along greater complexities in managing risk, which is clearly evident as the global financial crisis, initially triggered by sub-prime mortgages in the US, continues to unravel all over the world. The evolution of banks, quite like that of telecom companies, has entered a crucial phase that will decide their future.

4

Evolution of Merchants

Standing by a dry dock at the excavation sites of Lothal in Gujarat, it is hard to escape a sense of wonderment. Among the finds at this Indus Valley site, dating back to 2400 BC, were precisely designed weights and measures, which were a testimony to the highly evolved trade and commerce in those times. The dry dock itself underscored ship building and spoke of trade over a sea route to Mesopotamia. Of course, Lothal is not the earliest example of traders and merchants but it reminds us how they have been part of human endeavour for a very long time. Merchants selling goods and services have always depended on the communication technologies of the day no matter which era they lived in. We are told that in Lothal, for instance, it was possible that some leading members of the trading community might have funded shipbuilding as they stood to benefit from the opening up of new markets.

It was in 1498 that Portuguese explorer Vasco da Gama opened a sea route to India, which later became famous as the spice route. The evolution of merchants has its origin in complex trading arrangements that mainly emerged between 1500 and 1776, a period when many international trading laws came into existence. Holland, being the centre of trade in the sixteenth century, eschewed controls and supported free movement of goods. In 1592, Japan introduced foreign trading licences. In 1602, the Dutch East India Company was formed. Two years later, while Hugo Grotius published *Mare Liberum* (The Free Seas) advocating free trading on the seas by all nations, British parliament supported free trade but opposed the Dutch proposal for unfettered navigational rights.

From 1776 through 1995, when the World Trade Organization was created, world trade went through many upheavals, masking, as it often did, the imperial instincts of European nations. Even today, world trade continues to be embroiled over issues related to political considerations, masked by policies related to granting of subsidies and opening up of local markets for global trade.

Bilateral and multilateral agreements aside, world trade today is definitely driven by the ability to leverage global supply chains for local distribution. Merchandise and trade, which are very personalized in nature, have become intrinsically aligned with globalization. Whether it was the barter of commodities between the early settlers and natives of the land, or the rise of the colonial trading companies, or in more recent times, McDonald's dropping beef from all their burgers for select Asian markets, the emphasis has always been on leveraging supply chains and customizing goods or services for the local consumer.

Beyond globalization and personalization, merchandising has evolved to a point where retailers are not just focused on selling goods, but selling goods bundled with services. In the US, a large appliance retailer like Best Buy or Circuit City will resell appliances from marquee manufacturers, and will try its best to sell its customers its credit cards, gift cards, installation services and extended warranties, all of which represent high margin revenue streams for the store. Even furniture makers, whom you would not normally expect to sell services above and beyond their goods, offer services such as a warranty against stains on the upholstery and so on. Warranties, in particular, are motivated by higher revenues and profit margins but they have also brought a whole new dimension to merchant economics.

Beyond bundled services, the watchword now is 'recurring transactions' – the Gillette model of undercutting profitability on razors to make up margins through repeat sales of blades is now evident in so many different ways. One such example can be found in the electronic game industry, which, interestingly enough, touches upon several different verticals.

The console-based electronic game industry worldwide, estimated to be to the tune of $15 billion, is primarily contested by three large entities – Nintendo, Microsoft and Sony – with Nintendo and Sony being the incumbents, and Microsoft a relatively late entrant. The early business model focused on selling the actual gaming consoles or hardware at cost (or based on some reports, even at a loss) with real profitability for the manufacturers coming through repeat sales of the game cartridges, effectively delivering a recurring transaction-based business model.

That basic business model has now evolved to a point where the fundamental business drivers are still the game consoles and game cartridges, but ancillary industries have matured around game developers, game publishers, manufacturers and distributors of accessories, outlets that rent game cartridges, event managers that focus on hosting large game-related shows and contests, celebrities that endorse games that include their 'avatars', and marketing and advertising firms that focus specifically on product placement within games.

Under the pretence of electronic games, the larger battle being fought between Microsoft and Sony has more to do with who will eventually control the critical and highly lucrative home-entertainment gateway or hub. With Microsoft's Windows operating system installed on approximately nine out of ten personal computers in the workplace, it is safe to say that the enterprise world and effectively, the 'work window', is controlled by Microsoft (though companies ranging from Google to Oracle to Red Hat Linux are trying to change that). Beyond the 'work window', the other critical interface is the 'home window', which, in terms of tangible hardware in relatively recent times, has been dominated by personal computers, cable set-top boxes, and increasingly networked smart appliances.

With convergence as explained before, the most lucrative interface will soon be this 'home window', where both Microsoft and Sony are trying to position their respective gaming hardware as the home-entertainment hub of choice. Sony's most recent game console, the Playstation III, not only boasts of superior game logic and graphics, but is also being used to promote Blueray – Sony's new DVD technology and format. Today's gaming hardware, whether it is Microsoft's Xbox or Sony's Playstation, packs more firepower than some of the early supercomputers – hackers could very easily take today's gaming consoles and use them to predict the weather.

In the larger picture, once this home-entertainment hub or node is in place with broadband connectivity, the next step will be provisioning of personalized services, initially focused on information and entertainment or infotainment, and eventually scaling to all aspects, including education, health and personal finance – collectively lifestyle management.

Microsoft, Sony and Nintendo, with its recent successes with the Wii, are not the only entities focused on lifestyle management – it can be easily argued that becoming the lifestyle managers of choice for consumers is the holy grail of all merchandising. How else can you explain Walmart evolving from a department store to a super grocer, to potentially a bank offering retail banking products and financial services, with a lot more yet to come – it would not be a surprise if Walmart started offering clinical health services (it already has a pharmacy and optometrist in the premises) with resident doctors and outpatient services. And why not, if the outcome is a more personalized delivery of cost-effective goods and services to the consumers – is that not the promise of capitalism and free markets?

As discussed earlier in the context of banking, the Internet has also played a significant role in the evolution of merchants. From a global supply chain standpoint, the Internet has not only provided a more effective channel for flexing MRP, or material resource planning systems, and eventually ERP, or enterprise resource planning systems, but has also provided the necessary physical and systems level framework for inventory management and just-in-time practices, which have become critical to all manufacturers, distributors and resellers.

From the early days of ship-building in Lothal to MRP and ERP systems to the Internet for online requisitions and e-commerce to the extremely evolved (and hyped) B2B portals and bazaars to the use of RFID, or radio frequency identification tags, to track everything from raw material to finished goods, technology has always played an important role in trade. It is no surprise that Walmart's position as the world's largest retailer is largely (not entirely) because of its emphasis on the use of new and emerging technologies that help optimize its overall supply chain, eventually reducing overheads, and delivering the cost benefits in the form of lower prices to consumers.

Besides helping merchants chart unexplored territories, the Internet age has had an enormous impact on all areas of trade. It has increased transparency in dealings, be they business-to-business, business-to-consumer, business-to-government, or consumer-to-government, and, in the process, helped harmonize supply with actual demand on the ground, unlike in the past, when gauging the extent of the demand used to be often intuitive and therefore arbitrary. Enterprises in general and merchants in particular have been able to use the Internet to compress distribution and supply chains and increase customer touch points.

From some of the softer benefits related to enhancing productivity and offering a better work-life balance to employees through collaborative tools, to outsourcing of non-core functions and business processes with real-time interfaces for seamless product and service integration from multiple sources in numerous time zones, today the Internet has truly become the backbone of global trade.

Over and above supporting global trade, the Internet has enabled practically anyone, anywhere in the world, to distribute products and services to anyone, anywhere in the world. Initially, this resulted in everything from flowers(.com) to slippers(.com) being available over the Internet. Once the Internet bubble went bust, significantly drying up venture capital for pure-Internet plays, the industry matured, with several large Internet-based providers such as Amazon, eBay, Google and Yahoo! not only thriving but setting the trends, which a lot of traditional brick-and-mortar players are building on and leveraging for their respective businesses.

Brick-and-mortar entities, traditionally the forerunners of merchandising and retail, were pushed out of the limelight for a short period of time, with everyone declaring the dot-commers as the new and almighty rage. What many pure Internet-based service providers failed to realize was that as soon as a Walmart, Target, Macy's or Sears set up a website, not only did they have a web presence, they could also leverage all their channels, including their brick-and-mortar presence, to offer products, services, and promotions that used the Internet more effectively. There are already clear trends that the domination of Amazon and eBay may be ending with Walmart, Target Corp, Best Buy Co. and Circuit City Inc. pushing their way into the top ten sites frequented by shoppers.

Blending the Internet channel with brick-and-mortar presence is best exemplified through retailers like Carmax – consumers enjoy the benefits of reviewing automobile specifications, comparing prices and other parameters, looking at potential accessories and customizations, and even finalizing lenders, all in the comfort of their own home (or office), except the last but most important step of touching and feeling the goods before taking delivery from the dealer's physical lot. On a different note, Netflix has gained a lot of traction by allowing customers to view catalogues and rent movies online, with the DVDs being delivered through the existing postal system, all for a flat monthly fee for unlimited renting and viewing. Competition from Netflix and other similar providers (along with pressure from consumer groups) initially led to Blockbuster relaxing its late-fees policies, and has more recently led to announcements that Blockbuster will allow customers to order movies online, with the DVDs being delivered through its neighbourhood retail locations.

Specifically in the context of entertainment, the promise of the digital age is to deliver all content, on any device of choice ranging from the television set or cable box to personal computers to mobile phones (and some day your microwave oven!), completely devoid of any physical medium like a DVD or CD, either wirelessly over the air or through fibre optic and data cables already coming to most homes. The new AT&T, supported in particular by Microsoft on new technologies and standards related to IPTV, or Internet Protocol television, is banking on convergence of this nature. However, until that model becomes truly viable, Netflix and providers like them will keep putting more pressure on the Blockbusters of the world, in the process resulting in higher convenience at lower fees for consumers.

The most striking outcome of the Internet age has been the spectacular rise, and in some cases even fall, of online merchants and content providers. The ability to create virtual store fronts online and start selling goods and services that you do not own or offer is a remarkable feature of the evolution of merchants in the Internet age. Pure-Internet players such as Amazon, eBay, Google and Yahoo! have now become household names, with Google, in particular, evolving from a noun to a verb. Google's success, primarily built on unique advertising models, shows how much the Internet can be used to complement existing retail channels – both in the real as well as the virtual world. Common to all these entities is the fact that they have continuously innovated, leveraging the power of the Internet but recognizing that user adoption relies heavily on adding true value for all the stakeholders, starting with the consumer, through simple interfaces and creative business models.

Most of the successful Internet-based service providers now have plans to take their PC-based online models to the mobile channel. Google, Yahoo! and others already provide mobile phone users the ability to search for content, in some cases using web-based browsers customized for mobile phones, and in other cases through rich client-based applications that specialize in vertical searches as opposed to the traditional horizontal one. Monetization for these service providers typically occurs through advertising following search, and Google, in particular, is the market leader for the PC-based model.

Moving forward, a key challenge relates to the actual interface itself – the PC provides a lot more real estate (screen size) compared to the mobile phone, and hence is ideally suited to searching for content. On the other hand, the mobile phone is a lot better suited for time- and location- sensitive transactions. Hence it remains to be seen how some of these service providers alter their respective strategies as they go after the three times larger base of mobile phone users, leveraging their existing content and advertising assets.

As much as the Internet has played a phenomenal role in overall trade and commerce, merchandising is not just about e-commerce or online commerce. While the overall volume of commerce conducted online is growing exponentially, more so in the business-to-business space with the consumer-to-business space also increasing significantly year-on-year, the fact remains that over 90 per cent of all transactions are conducted in the real world – at a grocery store or at a gas station or at a department store or at a restaurant.

Merchants, largely in the real but increasingly in the virtual world, have always used promotions and sales to attract customers – one of the most common practices is to mail paper coupons directly to customers, or include them in newspapers and magazines. Beyond coupons, many merchants have special catalogues, which sometimes offer products that are not available anywhere else, including in their own retail outlets, creating a sense of exclusivity. Once again, with the Internet, all these options are now available online, including coupons and catalogues, with some Internet service providers focusing on aggregating coupons, allowing consumers to download and print them for redemption at the retail outlet.

It is estimated that in the US alone, over ten billion paper coupons are redeemed every year. Considering a hit rate of 2 per cent, which also is high, this means fifty times more paper coupons are actually issued by manufacturers and retailers. For all practical purposes, a paper coupon essentially becomes a cash-replacement instrument as it is responsible for delivering discounts on the sale price. Consequently, as one can imagine, an entire industry has evolved and matured around paper coupons – there are entities that focus just on designing and printing coupons, or issuing them, or collecting them. There are brokers and insurers of paper coupons, essentially settling the discounts with manufacturers before collecting from the retailers where the paper coupons were originally redeemed. Some manufacturers issue and acquire their own coupons, whereas others use third-party issuers and acquirers, and then there are merchants that offer their own in-store coupons as well as third-party manufacturer coupons. Similar to other cash-replacement instruments discussed earlier, this medium has its own dynamics, risks, fraud and costs, which eventually are borne by the consumer.

Along with paper coupons, another popular promotional channel used by merchants is that of rewards – one can get rewards for flying on a particular airline or collecting frequent flyer miles; rewards in the form of cash back by loyally using a particular credit card for purchases; rewards by staying at a hotel as frequently as possible. There are increasing cases of cross-selling between different service providers, where rewards collected through one channel can be redeemed in another channel. For example, one can collect rewards by using a credit card for (most kinds of) purchases and use the rewards towards procuring a ticket on a particular airline.

Between issuing and acquiring coupons for discounts and managing rewards, a very complicated and intricate industry has evolved, with entities like First Data Corporation and their partners playing a dominant role in supporting merchants with the necessary back end as well as front end systems. First Data, because of its somewhat behind-the-scenes neutral position, can often broker the right cross-selling and co-branding arrangements between diverse merchants that result in the kind of promotions we have become accustomed to these days. As much as the phenomena of coupons, rewards, cross-selling and co-branding are a highly evolved science in the US and parts of Europe and Asia, it is quickly catching on in other parts of the world with the overall rise in consumerism, supported by the growing buying power of the middle class and an increase in dispensable income ratios.

Leaving aside the argument that most transactions are still conducted in the real world, the flipside of e-commerce is the largely ignored question of what happens to those who do not have access to personal computers and the Internet. Of course, they always have the option of continuing to depend on the traditional ways of shopping at neighborhood stores. However, quite like the telecom have-nots, these people cannot enjoy the benefits of the New Age. While the combination of personal computers and the Internet has enhanced merchants' profitability and reach, increasing their ability to customize and personalize goods and services, the spread of smart mobile phones with Internet connectivity will exponentially increase overall access, but this time around to market segments that are even more diverse, requiring further innovation not only in the product and service offerings but in the overall delivery and business models.

The growth in opportunities and increased access, largely created through new technologies, has also meant increasing pressure on merchants, quite like telecom companies and banks, to retain customer loyalty and increase profitability. As a result, merchants have been increasingly forced to customize and personalize their merchandise in order to acquire new customers and retain existing ones.

Given all the progress over the years, ranging from globalization supported by trade agreements to new technologies and business models that marry the benefits of the brick-and-mortar world with the online world, to age-old practices of coupons and promotions being reinvented through increased cross-selling and co-branding, to the evolution of new channels for merchants to generate additional revenues and increase profitability, we believe the foundation is very much in place for merchants to leverage the unprecedented access available to the end user through mobile telephony.

In this context, it is important to look at Walmart. Due to the nature of the retail business, large merchants such as Walmart end up creating massive distribution infrastructure that lends itself to different kinds of businesses. The case of Walmart, the world's largest retailer, is a fascinating one, notwithstanding the withering criticism of its allegedly exploitative labour practices in developing countries from where it sources a large portion of its merchandise.

WALMART

The evolution of Walmart from the time it opened its first store in Rogers, Arkansas, in 1962 to today is a story most merchants can only aspire to. Seventeen years after it was founded, it notched up its first major success in posting sales in excess of a billion dollars. After that year, its growth was so phenomenal that in about the same time (eighteen years to be precise, between 1979 and 1997), it went on to achieve sales of $100 billion. Today, it is safe to state that Walmart has become the world's largest retailer. Hundreds of millions of people visit Walmart every week, which is more than the combined total of the number of tourists most countries receive every year.

With statistics like these, it is hard for the world outside the retail industry not to feel the sheer gravity of Walmart. With such large sums riding on its operations, one of the key features of Walmart's strategy is that it has learned to manage risk enough to develop ambitions beyond retail. It is hardly surprising then that Walmart wants to get into consumer banking. That ambition has caused quite a flutter within the banking industry.

Walmart has proposed an industrial loan corporation (ILC) in Salt Lake City, Utah. The idea of the ILC came into being around the turn of the last century to help consumers finance purchases. ILCs do not face many of the regulations that banks do.

In a country where starting a business almost never attracts political attention, Walmart's proposal prompted a lot of interest. So much so that the Federal Deposit Insurance Corporation (FDIC) felt compelled to look at the proposal closely. Detractors argued that if the FDIC approved Walmart's proposal, the store could essentially take over every aspect of American life.

'The nightmare scenario here is that Walmart controls every aspect of a community's economic life, both in the retail sector and the banking sector,' Chris Kofinis, spokesperson for the union-led campaign Wake-up Walmart, was quoted as saying to the media.

The reaction to Walmart's proposal also stems from the fact that the tradition-bound banking world does not like intruders. In this case, bankers feared that once Walmart got a banking licence, then similar to every other product and service it offered, it would apply downward pressure on the pricing of banking products and financial services, forcing other banks to start reducing their fees – something that consumers most definitely welcome, especially in the lower and middle classes.

While Walmart may be the most compelling example of how merchants have evolved, this has been the general trend in the US and elsewhere. Merchants have recognized that their business is not just about goods but also services as an add-on and recurring revenue source. Many of them have begun to recognize that globalization is a mixed blessing – it brings opportunities but also demands that products be customized in response to local needs. This would inevitably alter business models, but merchants sense an opportunity to emerge as lifestyle management providers as opposed to being neighbourhood stores with a limited number of attributes.

Akin to the realization among telecom companies and banks about the need for changing their traditional business models and bringing them in line with technological advances is the growing consciousness among merchants about the need to adapt to new ideas. They have to recognize that they can no longer stay content selling goods off their shelves. They have to ensure more recurring revenues by offering goods bundled with after-sale warranties for an extended period to create more revenues. While globalization has increased business opportunities for merchants, it has also brought about greater competition and the need to be flexible in response to local market conditions. New opportunities also mean more pressure on retaining customer loyalty because customers now have a greater choice than ever before.

Not only will merchants play a significant role in defining the new technologies and business models, but without their active support and participation no new transaction medium will ever be successful. As much as the telecom companies see themselves as the lifestyle management pipe providers, and banks see themselves as the lifestyle management fund providers, merchants truly have the opportunity to become the lifestyle management service providers, more so by riding on top of the existing global telecommunication and banking infrastructure, and joining the inevitable march of mobile money.

5

The Leather Wallet

There is an episode in the iconic American television sitcom *Seinfeld,* where one of the four main characters, George Costanza, played by actor Jason Alexander, has a serious problem managing his leather wallet overflowing with receipts and other pieces of paper. So much so that when he sits down with his wallet in one of the back pockets, he finds it impossible to balance himself. He sits elevated on one side. Even if one disregards the comedic exaggeration of the problem, most of us have faced a similar situation managing our leather wallets.

In its most basic sense, the leather wallet that most of us carry on us consists of an empty leather jacket, a plethora of plastic cards ranging from credit cards, bank cards, insurance cards, frequent flyer cards, driver's license, receipts, coupons and bills.

As one looks a little deeper, the leather wallet essentially represents an aggregation of highly personalized transaction tokens that are shared only between the issuers of the token and the user or owner of the token. Beyond these, the leather wallet also becomes a natural repository for other not so personalized tokens such as coupons. Paper receipts could arguably be stored anywhere but consumer behaviour dictates that they sit next to the cards or tokens that are used for conducting the transactions.

Historically, issuers of tokens have used them to acquire customers, and once acquired, to sell them various products and services. For example, every bank will have a benchmark for a particular market in terms of what its customer acquisition costs are, following which it has another benchmark dictating the return on that initial investment based on the various fees it will collect related to the various banking products and services it sells its customers. For many banks, the most lucrative product continues to be chequing accounts, and hence one now understands why banks have extremely elaborate marketing campaigns around its cheque cards or debit cards. The card in a leather wallet becomes an anchor for other not so tangible products and services to follow.

For a bank in particular, and every other issuer such as an insurance company or an airline, its card in the consumer's wallet represents an extremely critical link to providing various services to its customers. In an era when most consumers carry multiple credit cards or multiple frequent flyer cards, it is not uncommon for competing banks or airlines to vie for that much coveted top-of-the-stack spot in the consumer's leather wallet.

The next frontier in the quest for capturing consumers' minds and souls is in terms of mining their transaction records and usage behaviour, so as to offer even more targeted and personalized products and services, generating even more usage, fuelling even more offers, and so on. This is where receipts have a critical role to play.

Privacy advocates and regulators have been extremely vigilant in ensuring that consumers do not lose any sensitive personal data, as an entire industry has evolved around creating richer user profiles. As a case in point, the growing concern with Google's dominance in the search industry is related to the fact that it is collecting increasing amounts of data on users as they click on from one website to another unaware of the fact that in the background a detailed profile is being created and used to broker deals with advertisers, who in turn use these profiles to post offers for their wares. If a consumer's pattern of browsing websites can say so

much, one can imagine what all their receipts and transaction

records could say; this is the goldmine that all service providers would like to get their hands on.

Now we can see why George was hanging on to his over-stuffed wallet; it is a necessary and ubiquitous element of our daily lives, and the authors' quest (as that of many others) of digitizing this leather wallet to bring about convenience for the consumer has opened the proverbial Pandora's box. What became very obvious at the onset is that any digitization would require keeping some of the fundamental dynamics intact, namely, those between the consumers and issuers, and between the consumers and acquirers of these tokens and transactions.

The ideal digital wallet would have to entirely emulate this leather wallet; the leather wallet is what it is because of consumers and issuers. Hence it is imperative that all its key elements remain intact: leather wallet, cards, coupons, bills, et al, albeit now in a digital form, and with it bringing about greater convenience, flexibility, security and efficiencies.

The advent of the Internet, specifically electronic commerce, began subtly changing the role and utility of the leather wallet. Sensing a clear opportunity, some technology companies developed what came to be known as server-based wallets, which were a sort of virtual and remote instruments of payments that you could maintain online and use as and when you needed them. A lot of the functionalities that one could perform by using the traditional leather wallet could now be performed with the click of a few buttons. The Internet also afforded the ability to electronically store a transaction trail, including the receipts on your PC or laptop. But server-based wallets, although promising, had their own flaws. They did not extend to the real world, where the bulk of transactions are conducted even today. The fact that they did not provide consumers the same experience as they were used to, with their leather wallets and cards or tokens being stored in the intermediaries' domain, went against them.

The next step was the emergence of mobile phones, with considerable capabilities to execute many of the functionalities that were possible only on PCs or laptops earlier. One major advantage that mobile phones offered over laptops and PCs was that they were far more personal, and when it came to emulating leather wallets, a lot more mobile. With phones becoming smaller and sleeker, carrying them in one's pocket, quite like the leather wallet, was a major plus. By early 2000, the time was becoming ripe for mobile phones to fulfil the functions of the traditional leather wallet.

Meanwhile, with a growing number of credit cards, debit cards, airline cards, insurance cards, stored-value cards and coupons, leather wallets have become a modern nightmare. Add to all this the cumbersome process of carrying cheque books, managing bank accounts, maintaining receipts and filing expense reports, and you have the perfect recipe for a stress-related disaster. A lot of us do not realize the amount of time we spend in managing day-to-day finances and account keeping. As we finish one cycle of paying monthly bills, the next cycle begins almost immediately. It seems like a vicious circle we can never get out of.

When personal computers became popular in the 1980s, a lot of people thought managing life would become much easier since the machine could do many chores simultaneously and much faster. While that view was broadly accurate, the fact that the machine was deskbound created its own limitations. As laptops emerged and Internet access became widely available, the problem of being mobile while carrying out routine transactions was solved to a considerable degree. However, no matter how small and light, laptops were still not an ideal tool to ensure easy mobility and efficient execution of various transactions. When mobile phones were first introduced for commercial purposes in 1973, very few people had the imagination to ascribe to them a role that they have since gone on to play, especially during the last three to five years. Very few people could extrapolate from the existing technology in the 1970s and 1980s, and even in the 1990s, that mobile telephones would one day become as powerful as PCs. The advent of Java-enabled smart phones by 2001 raised hopes among the early speculators that mobile phones would eventually have the potential to become a serious alternative to PCs.

It is a measure of how rapidly technologies change that as recently as 2000, an article in *Java World*, written by John Rommel, said: 'I predict that by next year Java will be the major wireless development platform. Your Walkman, personal digital assistant (PDA), Internet, wallet, and favourite video game will reside in a box smaller than a portable phone.' Rommel foresaw that today's portable phone, with computing power equivalent to Intel 386 microprocessors, would continue to obey Moore's Law, doubling in power every eighteen months. Java already provided the capabilities needed to write meaningful software applications on those devices. Those applications included games, investment portfolios, calendars, and other types of software realized from the imaginations of creative developers. 'Our future world will be connected to wireless devices running Java applets,' wrote Rommel. Any application that could run on a PC, he added, could potentially run on a portable phone. 'Java applets are the perfect way to run content-rich applications, since they offer a way of delivering more information and more control of the data sent to your handheld device,' Rommel concluded.

In less than six years, not only has that vision come true but has surpassed itself. Increasing computing power, bigger displays, faster Internet connectivity, cheaper call charges and growing awareness among customers are all creating an ecology where the mobile phone is becoming a viable and, in many ways, more scalable alternative to the PC and the laptop to conduct transactions.

The emergence of mobile phones as a serious alternative to PCs and laptops will be driven by many applications. One of these will be people's ability to receive and pay bills directly from their mobile phones. While traditionally advanced markets such as Japan and Korea have already stolen a march over the rest, there are clear signs that the US will take this technology forward in a major way. Unlike the Japanese and Korean markets, which are substantial, the US market has the advantage of size. It has been a tradition with the US market to focus heavily on standardization when it comes to any new technology. Once relevant standards are in place, the adoption of the technology becomes far easier. It also allows for more rapid and seamless scalability. A big advantage of this approach is that adoption and scaling of the technology becomes much easier then in other parts of the world.

One interesting aspect of the mobile revolution is that in many parts of the world, people who were left out during the evolution of basic telephony have now been propelled into the most modern age of mobile telephony with features that many US operators were unable to offer till recently. This leapfrogging is helping drive the growth of mobile phones as an instrument of transactions in Asia, Middle East and Africa.

Seeing the manner in which communication technologies have grown, it would seem that there is a subtly orchestrated plan at work. No one quite understands who the planner is but somehow technologies evolve and fit together in such a way that one is tempted to think of it as part of a consciously laid-out design. Of course, we know that is not the case. Take, for example, the emergence of the mobile phone as much more than just a phone. Although the concept of the mobile wallet had been in existence since the mid-1990s, till about the advent of the twenty-first century, there was no serious attempt by telecom companies or handset manufacturers to incorporate that idea. But suddenly, over the past few years, there has been a dramatic shift in favour of the mobile wallet. Since the market leaders in the US are now pushing for the mobile wallet, it is expected to grow exponentially and become a feature intrinsic to the mobile phones soon. Those who have been involved with mobile wallet technology understood a long time ago that it was not just about the ability to carry out financial transactions directly from the mobile phone that would attract attention but, equally, non-financial transactions in the domains of government, security, health, universities and so on.

We looked at the leather wallet earlier as a repository of personalized tokens – cards, coupons, bills, receipts, etc. The combination of a leather wallet and mobile phone or mobile wallet is not only a repository of tokens but can also become a repository of applications. Effectively, every token in a mobile wallet now has an associated application – for example, a credit card or bank card can extend to complete online or mobile banking, giving the user the ability to check balances and move funds in real time, anytime and anywhere, within three clicks on his or her mobile phone. Similarly, a frequent flyer card extends into a complete airline ticketing and loyalty application, enabling a user to book, buy and download a ticket directly through the mobile phone. Such extensions hold great promise for the user as well as the service provider; the user can now more effectively manage his or her increasingly complicated life, whereas the service provider can reduce costs for supporting customers or not having to pay intermediaries.

The following graphic depicts the evolution of a singular application such as mobile banking: while the top graphic shows an example of an early, fairly simplistic approach to providing online banking through mobile phones, the bottom one shows a more recent example of mobile banking that was unveiled in Asia.

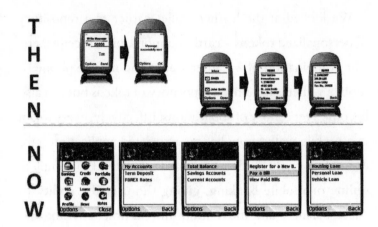

MOBILE BANKING USER INTERFACE

It is evident from the above graphic that the mobile wallet has indeed come of age, that today similar mobile wallets are in commercial use for booking and buying railway and airline tickets, conducting online banking transactions, paying bills, conducting cross-border remittances or money transfer, topping up stored-value accounts, downloading coupons, purchasing through actionable advertisements, and paying at retail stores.

We firmly believe that from the standpoint of a consumer, any scalable mobile wallet will need to imbibe all the critical building blocks of the leather wallet to achieve the same level of ubiquity, namely the empty jacket, or, in case of a mobile wallet, a simple and intuitive user interface that mimics the leather wallet metaphor; multiple cards or, in case of a mobile wallet, images and branding as per existing cards; the ability to conduct transactions seamlessly in the real and virtual worlds or, in case of a mobile wallet, to transact using a common interface in proximity as well as remote environments; and the ability to store receipts or, in case of a mobile wallet, store and archive receipts in digital form.

Similarly, from the issuer's standpoint, it will want to continue issuing its cards and tokens, now in electronic form, securely, wirelessly and directly to the consumer's mobile wallet, without any disintermediation. Acquirers of cards and coupons will want to ensure they can use their existing settlement infrastructure to process transactions initiated from mobile wallets, the same way they process transactions initiated by plastic cards or paper coupons.

Ensuring that the requirements of the consumer, merchant, issuer and acquirer are met is not a simple task, especially when one factors in legacy infrastructure, standards and special interests. The technology required to emulate a complete leather wallet needs to ensure that the user interface is simple and intuitive for the consumer, and, at the same time, provides a scalable and secure framework whereby several disparate token issuers and application providers can come together without compromising their individual business models, and security and risk management. Simply put, a mobile wallet with fifty distinct cards, coupons, bills and applications would need a highly secure, scalable and robust platform that can manage fifty different security schemes.

Hence it is no surprise that despite billions of dollars invested into m-commerce, there is yet to emerge a truly scalable model of transacting in the real and virtual world using mobile phones. But it is only a matter of time before this happens.

6

Early Experiments

Stanley Kubrick and Arthur C. Clarke's *2001: A Space Odyssey*, released in 1968, introduced several iconic concepts that have intrigued technocrats and geeks of all ages. These include HAL the computer, space shuttles and space stations. The film is also credited with introducing the smart card. It would be a stretch in the current context of electronic and mobile commerce to extend some of the early experiences back to 1968, but the fact remains that the industry has been seeking a more intelligent successor to the plastic magnetic stripe card, or mag-stripe card, for several decades.

To better understand smart cards and the broader subject of electronic commerce, it is important to deconstruct the magnetic stripe card. In its most basic sense it is a card with some branding and imagery, with a magnetic stripe on the back that is encoded with data specific to the issuer and user of the card. When this card is swiped against a stationary sensor that can read this magnetic data, the sensor serially transmits this issuer and user data over the telecommunication infrastructure to initiate and eventually settle a transaction.

As is the case with cash, cash alternative instruments like magnetic stripe cards have been misused and abused from the onset, and hence authentication of the user or card holder in real time has been of great importance both for merchants as well as the issuers and acquirers of these cards. User authentication in real time is one of the pivotal variables for financial service providers in their risk management models, which drives everything from what commission rate to apply for existing merchants to what new markets to pursue. Some markets, like the US, have had better telecommunication infrastructure and hence could quickly build a real-time authentication system. In contrast, several European markets struggled on this front and faced relatively more cases of fraud related to payment cards.

It was this need for a better real-time authentication scheme that led to the development of EMV Cards (Euro MasterCard Visa), or smart cards. Fundamentally, smart cards are plastic cards with an integrated circuit that provides what the industry calls tamper-proof storage of issuer and user credentials. These credentials can be used for conducting payment just as one would from a magnetic stripe card, or for storing loyalty or health information. The credentials can be read by special sensors, and typically require a personal identification number or PIN to be entered at the point of sale to initiate and settle the transaction.

POINT-OF-SALE TERMINAL

In the area of smart cards, two names that attracted a lot of attention were Multos and Mondex. Multos was developed as a secure smart card operating system, while Mondex was developed in the early 1990s as an electronic cash system based on smart cards. With an embedded computer chip, Mondex allowed smart cards to be programmed for a set of applications, including storing a cash equivalent component on the card for small ticket transactions. SUN used its popular Java programming language to develop the Java Card platform for empowering developers to build applications for these cards.

A significant industry exists today around smart cards, which are being used for several applications. Although smart cards made considerable headway in European markets, they performed dismally in the US, arguably the most important market for any new technological innovation. A combination of factors worked against smart cards, including the lack of interactivity in the user interface and the failure to take into account the interests of all the stakeholders. As the US had traditionally better communication capabilities and, consequently, real-time settlement for magnetic stripe cards, merchants and issuers did not see a real need to invest in this new technology, which, in addition to distributing the smart cards, required a new set of retail terminals and support.

With the emergence of the mobile phone as a truly personal device with greater interactivity, processing capability, tamper-proof storage and connectivity, the utility of smart cards in their current form seems to be limited. But in our historical analysis it is important to catalogue the smart card as one of the early attempts to evolve the one-dimensional plastic card into a multi-dimensional digital wallet. We must give Arthur C. Clarke and Stanley Kubrick credit for triggering another great innovation.

By the late 1990s, an atmosphere began building up in favour of e-commerce, with people being able to use the Internet to shop and make payments using their credit cards. Some early successful B2B, or business-to-business, models were quickly modified for B2C, or business-to-consumer, applications. Like all experiments, this one too was troubled by several inefficiencies. There were frequent consumer complaints that they had to fill out complicated order forms before they could complete their purchases. The early order forms were tedious as they required detailed information to ensure security. According to a survey conducted at the time by a New York-based research firm, Jupiter Communications Inc., some 27 per cent of shoppers abandoned an online order because of the complicated order forms.

It was in 1998 that technology companies began to experiment with what they called 'server-based wallets', essentially a web-based server that would hold all the credentials and settle transactions with online or Internet-based merchants on behalf of the user. It was then that a company named GlobeSet introduced a digital wallet loaded onto a server of a service provider. The company said their wallet was in compliance with the Secure Electronic Transactions (SET) protocol, which was accepted by both MasterCard and Visa. The server-based wallet was described as easy to use and secure.

The server wallet was heralded as a technology that would speed up secure credit card-based transactions on the Net and, in the process, strengthen e-commerce. Although such wallets did make some inroads among consumers, the penetration was nowhere close to what was initially expected. Server-side wallets were said to prevent merchant fraud since they used certificates to verify the identity of all parties. Despite claims of ease of use and security, such wallets enjoyed a limited spread at best. One of the reasons cited was the lack of uniform standards. In 1999, major vendors such as America Online Inc., Microsoft Corp., and Sun Microsystems Inc., endorsed a new standard called E-Commerce Modelling Language (ECML), which offered online merchants a standardized way to collect electronic data for shipping, billing and payment. Industry analysts then believed that by 2001, server-based wallets would pick up momentum. That did not quite happen.

One of the big stories in the late 1990s was that of Brokat, a company based in Germany, which rose and fell spectacularly despite having good technology and support from the industry. This ecommerce software maker was once regarded by *Time* as one of the thirty hottest companies in Europe. In 2001, despite all the promise, Brokat began insolvency proceedings, saying it was unable to negotiate a restructuring agreement with creditors.

Simultaneously, MasterCard and Visa developed their own

standards to strengthen the security of online transactions. MasterCard created SecureCode, while Visa developed 3D Secure. MasterCard's SecureCode is like a private code that prevents unauthorized use of credit cards. The code is similar to what people use during ATM transactions. It is an added layer of security because it requires a customer code to be confirmed before a transaction is complete. Visa, on the other hand, introduced 3D Secure, which referred to security in three domains – Visa account information security, Visa authenticated payment and best business practices. Both card companies were essentially driven by concerns about the rising incidence of chargeback, which meant people would dispute a 'fraudulent' charge and would want to be compensated. Chargeback also lent itself to frequent misuse.

Despite server-based wallets holding great promise and attracting significant investments at the time, looking back it is now easy to see that these server wallets failed to address three fundamental transaction requirements: the user interface did not mimic the leather wallet and for the most part forced the consumer to adopt a new type of interface; the credentials or cards were stored on a server somewhere on the Internet and not on the user's mobile phone, where she or he was used to storing them; the usability was restricted only to online merchants and could not be extended easily into the real world, where more than 90 per cent of all transactions are still conducted.

Although server-based wallets did not quite attain the success they were initially projected to, refinements over the years have helped them gain some traction within closed-loop situations, such as one-click payment solutions for web-stores. Closed-loop solutions are intrinsically limited because the server-based wallet for one provider cannot be used on another's site or web-store, and vice versa. Notably, some leading players, such as IBM and Microsoft, have tried to develop an open-loop solution, a sort of universal server-based wallet, but it has not worked so far mainly due to privacy concerns, with users worried that all their personal information stored in a single location could potentially be hacked or misused by the entities managing them.

Another attempt at a universally acceptable solution was the creation of a universal secure web-service-based ID management and federated ID management. In early 2000, the industry warmed up to the idea of a possible adoption of identity federation standards and interoperability of enterprise-level products. Earlier, a new 'Web Services Federation Language (WS-Federation)' specification was published to enable an identity, account, attribute, authentication, and authorization federation across different trust realms. It was in this context that there emerged the Liberty Alliance Project, an alliance of more than 150 companies and non-profit and government organizations from across the world, to develop 'an open standard for federated network identity that supports all current and emerging network devices.' According to the alliance, 'Federated identity offers businesses, governments, employees and consumers a more convenient and secure way to control identity information in today's digital economy... it is a key component in driving the use of e-commerce and personalized data services, as well as web-based services.'

Electronic money or e-money was a new and attractive feature of the digital revolution during the mid- to late-1990s. In those days it was believed that consumers would be wary of providing their credit card numbers while making a purchase. Instead, customers were given an alternative to convert physical cash to the digital variety, which would be stored offline on cards embedded with a chip or inside a computer's hard drive. That e-money in turn would be used to make purchases via the Internet.

Several private digital currency start-ups such as Beenz. com, Flooz.com and Goldmoney.com came into being, but they had one fundamental flaw. They were not connected to any government system or central banks that guaranteed security. That turned off a lot of people. One compelling example of this trend was PayPal. It was founded in 1998 by Peter Thiel and Max Levchin. In a feature that perhaps underscored the break from tradition was PayPal's positioning itself as a service to beam money via PDAs.

As if to emphasize its uniqueness, the company hired *Star Trek* actor James Doohan, who immortalized the character Scotty. Notwithstanding the USP of Scotty selling a way to beam a payment, that version of PayPal did not quite go far. It was soon changed into a web-based service, which gained enormous popularity with eBay's millions of users. Interestingly, despite its success in a new avatar, PayPal was reportedly losing $10 million a month. It fell prey to identity thieves from outside America, resulting in a loss of millions of dollars. However, after its initial problems and its 2002 takeover by eBay, PayPal went on to become a powerful alternative to existing cash-replacement instruments and providers. This was even as PayPal's competitors, such as Citibank's c2it, Western Union's BidPay, and Yahoo!'s PayDirect, fell by the wayside. BidPay was acquired in 2006 by CyberSource Corporation and was positioned again as a competitor to PayPal. In March 2006, PayPal, building on its success because of eBay backing, launched its mobile version called PayPal Mobile.

PayPal turned out to be the only major player to not just survive the 2002 dotcom bust but perhaps emerge stronger. The phase of server-based wallets saw many players rise out of nowhere and decline precipitously. While some companies began as server-based wallets but went on to offer either a general transaction platform or a different set of applications, many were wiped out without a trace. However, in the process, the industry learned many valuable lessons. In the early days, many thought that given the rise of Internet-based transactions, security would by itself become big business. The emergence of companies such as VeriSign was heralded as a whole new business model based on providing security to Internet-based transactions. Somewhere along the line, the industry lost sight, only to regain it later, that the real business was not security but the overriding applications.

With the evolution of mobile phones, smart cards, and e-commerce, not necessarily in that order, it was inevitable that a smart card would be integrated into the mobile phone to conduct e-commerce or, as more aptly termed, m-commerce, or mobile commerce. Early experiments in Europe did exactly that, as mobile phones allowed smart cards to be inserted into the actual handset, with the smart card storing and managing the transaction instrument and the phone providing real-time connectivity to the online merchant. Soon these experiments led to storing the transaction credentials on the mobile phone's SIM (or subscriber identity module) card instead of a separate smart card.

As it became obvious to the telecom companies and banks that this was the next frontier of growth, both in terms of new users as well as new value-added services, the fight over customer acquisition and control became even more intense. Telecom companies wanted to become banks and vice versa.

Telecom companies wanted to capture this critical customer acquisition channel, or the payment card information stored on the SIM, manage it and capitalize on it, in essence forcing themselves between the banks and the consumers. The banks were alert to this strategy all along, and hence came an era in mobile commerce that saw extreme experiments, such as mobile phones with two different SIMs, one for the telecom companies and the other for the bank, both managing their own credentials and maintaining their own control over the consumer. Needless to say, none of these experiments scaled successfully.

Along with the propagation of server wallets as the next big application, there was also a virtually parallel movement to use mobile phones for conducting proximity transactions, such as buying a can of Coke at a vending machine or paying for a train ticket at a subway station. While early experiments did prove that such proximity transactions could be carried out, in the strictest terms they were not really proximity transactions. They were more like closed-loop transactions where a consumer's mobile phone would call Coke's centralized system, which in turn would get in touch with an individual vending machine, which would eventually dispense a can. In effect, several messages had to be zapped in real time between the cell phone, a service provider and a vending machine or turnstile. Not only did this assume that these messages could be delivered in real time with considerable reliability but also that the business model could accommodate such an overhead. It was not feasible to scale such models, especially for vending machines that dispense soda cans and snacks, which, in many cases, are in basements where over-the-air connectivity is poor, and service providers do not have enough margins to sustain the additional cost associated with zapping numerous messages back and forth.

By early 2000, several pieces of mobile commerce with considerable promise were floating around without any serious attempt to bring them under one cohesive structure. One such piece was the prepaid phone card and airtime top-up. Prepaid phone cards were physical cards that consumers would buy at telecom company outlets and retail locations. Users would scratch the card to obtain a unique number, which in turn would be used to activate either a new account or add more minutes to an existing one. Airtime top-up required consumers to personally go to an outlet and recharge the account. While the prepaid airtime segment of the market has grown rapidly, with some mobile carriers claiming almost 80 per cent prepaid subscribers compared to only 20 per cent postpaid ones, its delivery by and large remains cumbersome. The problem with physical scratch-off cards, which, despite several alternative channels such as topping up online and ATMs, remain popular, is not just that it is cumbersome and error-prone for subscribers, but that it is also is a fairly expensive mode of distribution for the telecom companies, with retailers charging relatively large commissions for stocking these cards on their shelves.

Distribution of prepaid airtime soon became an industry by itself, and has continued to grow, with several technology providers, application service providers, banks, and telecom companies jumping in with all kinds of innovative solutions. In many ways, this specific application of topping up airtime, in particular using the mobile phone and a cash alternative payment instrument, broadened the definition of mobile commerce. Earlier, m-commerce was used to describe browsing the Internet through a wireless or mobile device. Now the industry started looking at several such person-to-business or person-to-person payment and transaction applications under the broad label of m-commerce.

In the late 1990s, banks began to understand the potential of making many of their routine enquiry-based services, such as account balance, available on the Internet. Most banks understood the importance of the Net-based services because they felt they could charge a convenience fee from their customers. Of course, as Internet banking eventually evolved into enabling fund transfers, most banks made such services free.

Like proximity transactions such as buying a Coke at a vending machine or a train ticket at a subway station,

technology experts saw clear possibilities of extending online banking services to mobile phones. In the early days, this was hamstrung by a lack of transaction technology as well as security concerns. A way out was using the short messaging service (SMS) on the mobile to satisfy basic banking requirements. The way SMS worked was that a customer would send a short message containing key words such as 'bal' for balance to his or her bank. The bank in turn would send an SMS with the required information to the customer's mobile. One of the constraints of using SMS was that it did not allow for real-time banking functionalities, such as money transfers and wire transfers, to be carried out from the mobile phones. This was primarily because such transactions were far more complex than just finding out the bank balance, and required very high levels of security.

Such basic SMS-based services were soon replaced by secure SMS transactions powered by applications written and stored on the SIM, popularly referred to as SIMTk, or SIM Toolkit-based services. Even today, many SMS- and Unstructured Supplementary Service Data or USSD-based services remain relevant and are used in several commercial deployments. In early 2000, a card billed as 'the world's most advanced mobile phone SIM card' was introduced. The 1MB SuperSIM card had been developed for TIM, the leading Italian mobile operator, by Oberthur Card Systems, one of the world's leading providers of smart card-based solutions, and STMicroelectronics, one of the leading suppliers of silicon chip technology. Till the introduction of that card, SIM cards were used to store text-based information, including subscriber authentication information as well as personal phone directories and messages. With the rise of 3G phones, demand began growing for richer content, such as MMS and pictures. With that came the necessity for SIM cards that could store more data.

'The new 1MB SuperSIM enables us to add a variety of 3G multimedia proposals to the exciting services already offered by our InteracTIM engine. It represents the latest step of an evolution started some years ago that brought TIM to pass, in less than thirty months, from a 32K card to the newest SIM-Plus 128K ... up to this very first innovative product that will revolutionize the mobile telephone market. This unequalled success has been possible thanks to the strong partnership that TIM has always developed with its card manufacturers and chip makers and that, based on this innovative product, will soon bring other important innovations related to smart card technologies,' Paolo Paganucci, smart card manager of TIM, was quoted as saying by Smart Card Alliance.

There is an offshoot of SMS known as the Premium SMS (PSMS), predominantly in use in Asia and Europe. Although PSMS uses the same network as SMS, it has additional

features that let the user view informational data, including

stocks, sports scores, travel information and so on. In Asia and Europe, SMS has grown into a strong commercial feature, and is expected to endure for quite some time. In countries like India and Japan, it has also emerged as a preferred means of communication among friends and family.

SMS-based transaction solutions have been in use in many countries but they still do not provide the same level of convenience and ease as being able to directly communicate with a service provider or a bank from one's cell phone. Most of these solutions, be they SMS-based or the inaccurately called proximity transactions, such as buying a soda can at a vending machine, or, for that matter, the Internet-based server wallets, did not offer the kind of user experience needed for a new technology to spread quickly.

Most of these options failed because they offered a limited number of functionalities and were devoid of an intuitive experience. Also, none of them offered multiple options in terms of payment instruments. It has been universally observed that consumers do not like being offered just one way of making payments. If there was a way to be able to choose from more than one option on the mobile phone, it would open doors both for consumers as well as telecom companies, banks and merchants.

iMode in Japan, launched by NTT DOCOMO, was revolutionary in several aspects. It made it easier for existing online merchants to scale to the mobile channel by providing

107

a similar scripting language (and unlike WAP, or wireless application protocol, not forcing them to adopt a brand new language). It also made it worth their time and effort by providing different business models. iMode gained huge traction in Japan, while WAP has lagged for several reasons. However, NTT DOCOMO's attempt of replicating the iMode model using FeliCa, or Near Field Communication or NFC-based platform, has not been as successful as it lacks some of the fundamental aspects of the leather wallet metaphor.

Moving beyond SMS and WAP-based transactions, the industry gradually started rallying around two key aspects – client-based applications for mobile phones and true proximity transactions. Client-based applications, especially powered by SUN's Java-based platform (J2ME) with over a billion compatible mobile handsets today, as well as other platforms from Microsoft, Symbian, Qualcomm, and more recently, Apple and Google, significantly improve usability and security, supporting a huge community of developers that can now leverage a relatively open distribution channel. Handset manufacturers like Nokia have a roadmap to embed web application servers on all their handsets, creating the underlying infrastructure for every mobile phone to become a unique node on a global network, and accessing or powering varied applications from media to payments to social networks.

After some faulty starts, proximity transactions now have been standardized over NFC (FeliCa in Japan), and unlike some of the early attempts at zapping messages back and forth, will now power true proximity transactions in the real world. The technology is commercial in Japan and Korea and has been piloted extensively in North America and Europe. Beyond the technology, banks have now started launching contactless RF plastic cards, essentially to start changing user behaviour, which for several decades has been centred on swiping of plastic cards, and to enable merchants to replace or augment magnetic stripe terminals with contactless RF readers. Consumers will be asked to wave or tap their plastic cards instead of swiping them, and once the NFC handsets are in the market, they will be asked to wave or tap their phones instead of cards at the same merchant readers.

With the introduction of the iPhone by Apple, with a far superior user interface and mobile phone browser, the debate of using browsers over native applications on mobile phones has been reignited. It may be safe to say that whereas a superior browser like the one on the iPhone will definitely be the way to go for open content, native or client applications may still be a necessity for personalized services that require a different level of security on the mobile phone compared to the PC.

Over the years, with the learnings from previous eras, several solutions and models have evolved. On one hand there are some successes in select regions, like Paybox in Germany and Austria, or Smart in the Philippines, which have scaled to a large number of users but have not yet scaled beyond their regions of influence. M-PESA, a mobile phone-based person-to-person payment system launched by Safaricom, a dominant telecom company in Kenya, is rapidly gaining popularity, and according to the company, is now being exported to other regions across Africa and Asia.

More recently, there have been attempts to create mobile banking platforms centred around telecom companies, similar to Simpay in Europe, which was launched with great fanfare only to collapse a couple of years later. The jury is still out on some of these new experiments but based on previous learnings, if they continue to provide one-dimensional services, they will end up going the same way as Brokat or Simpay.

In summary, whether we start tracking the evolution of the digital wallet from the introduction of the smart card or server-based wallets or SIM-based solutions or one-dimensional mobile banking platforms, the lack of mass adoption can almost always be traced back to the lack of meeting some of the fundamental dictates of the leather wallet metaphor. It could be a complicated user interface and set up, one-of-a-type payment, one-of-a-type application, limited transaction capability, non-scalable business models, and further disintermediation between the principal service provider and consumer. As the inevitable march towards digitizing money continues, it is important to better understand this somewhat simplistic leather wallet, often taken for granted but yet so elusive.

7

Smart Phones

Since the introduction of the first commercial mobile radio phone service in 1946 in Saint Louis, Missouri, by AT&T and Southwestern Bell, cell phones have mainly remained an instrument to exchange voice. The early cell phones were bulky and cumbersome to carry. Motorola, for instance, had a television commercial in the early 1990s that highlighted how sturdy the instrument was rather than what it could do. In that commercial, the Motorola phone would be dropped down a staircase and it would still be working. The first-generation or 1G phones, like Motorola's Dynatac 8000X, were quite cumbersome to carry but were a dramatic departure from the legacy landline phones.

Early mobile phone instruments were as much a product of materials available then as they were of the core technology components, namely the display, the chipsets, the battery and the casing. Starting with a bare monochrome display in the first-generation handsets that would support simple characters, today's mobile phones support high-resolution colour television broadcasts streaming live over the air. The first-generation handsets had simple chipsets, which have now been replaced with high-speed DSPs or digital signal processors. Current handsets, similar to personal computers, have read only memory, random access memory, as well as removable memory. With ever growing features and functionalities, battery life for mobile phones continues to be stretched. The early handsets were bulky and the comparison to a 'brick' was apt; today, handsets are not only smaller but the casing and styling are customized with different colours, styles and textures to suit different demographics – a pink phone for adolescent girls, a silver metallic finish for yuppies, and larger keypads for senior citizens!

As the processing power of chips began to grow, phone makers saw possibilities of doing a little more than just providing the talk facility on their instruments. Processing power grew in inverse proportion to the size of the chip, and consequently, speeded up miniaturization of phones. Every year since the early 1990s, phones have become progressively smaller, smarter and more powerful. A major leap came when mobile phones became small enough to fit into one's pocket.

With rising processing power in terms of number crunching capability and a large amount of memory, it was only a matter of time before the mobile phone started to appear as the ubiquitous personal computer. Phones became smarter with embedded operating systems similar to those on the PC.

Phone operating systems range from proprietary, such as from BlackBerry, to the more common variety such as Linux, Symbian and Windows. As consumers started to look for more applications beyond making voice calls from their mobile phones, the industry was forced to evolve the handsets and underlying technologies, and the trend continues today.

Manufacturers started integrating a number of functional hardware subsystems into the phone to convert the voice-only phone to an equivalent of the 'Swiss knife', by making available to consumers items such as texting, music player, recorder, video camera, radio, Bluetooth connectivity, WiFi, Near Field Communication (NFC), and Global Positioning System (GPS).

As mobile phones evolved, telecom companies that provided the connectivity to them realized that by carefully controlling the features on the handsets, they could in turn

drive a hardware-based revenue stream in addition to the

services they provided. The industry collectively sells about a billion new mobile phones worldwide every year, making the mobile phone the single largest consumer appliance to be produced, delivered and supported.

The rise of browsers and spread of the Internet in the early 1990s opened up more possibilities for mobile phones. Leveraging the powerful processor and the associated hardware and operating system, manufacturers were able to offer a variety of applications.

One of the most useful applications was the browser. Some phones now have browsers functionally similar to those prevalent on laptop and desktop computers, alleviating the learning curve. Power and convenience of 'mobile browsing' has added tremendous value to the mobile phone. A number of websites now include mobile-friendly content, making it easier to access information, play interactive games and even perform transactions.

Most high-end smart phones include applications targeted at professionals, thus closing the functional gap between PCs and smart phones. It is now possible to seamlessly exchange MS Word, Excel and Adobe PDF documents between the computer and phone. Productivity applications, such as those for managing contacts, schedules, reminders, to-do lists, have also became commonplace. As smart phones evolved in terms of their capacity to store data – contacts, schedules, music, photographs, video clips, documents, etc.

– it was imperative to include mechanisms for information exchange between smart phones and also between a smart phone and a PC. Early models used a slow serial interface and required wired connections. More recent models now support wireless sync capabilities with PCs as well as with subscription-based web services.

Soon after that there began a significant evolution in proximity technologies on the phone, such as Infrared and Bluetooth. The emergence of Bluetooth, a specification for personal area networks that allows connectivity and exchange of information between mobile phones and other devices such as laptops, PDAs and PCs, brought a whole new dimension to the phones. Suddenly, what was till then a collection of stand-alone devices became seamlessly connected, creating a whole new universe.

With advantages of higher data rates and no constraints of line-of-sight requirement, Bluetooth became the dominant mode for close-range communication. A number of newer models have, therefore, dropped Infrared as a standard interface.

As connectivity grew among devices, designers saw possibilities of merging PDAs with phones and creating smart phones. More recent phones include WiFi and WIMAX bands to further enhance speed and convenience of data transfer. On-the-go USB has now become standard on most contemporary smart phones.

While camera resolutions on early phone models were low – between 1 and 2 megapixels – the gap between the stand-alone digital camera and the camera smart phone has shrunk considerably. At the time of writing, camera phones with resolutions in the range of 8 megapixels are becoming common. The USB On-The-Go interface makes it possible to print pictures in standard high-resolution printers.

Almost parallel to these developments, there were advances being made in software. The advent of Java, specifically the J2EE and J2ME platforms, led to mobile phones acquiring a powerful channel for downloading third-party applications directly over the air.

While programming languages such as C & C++ dominated development of native applications, particularly on phones with Windows and Linux operating systems, Java gained ground on phones based on the Symbian and BREW operating environments.

The introduction of Wireless Application Protocol (WAP), a specification that allows users to instantly access information via handheld devices, and Wireless Markup Language (WML), a language facilitating the presentation of text from web pages on cell phones and other hand-held devices, were expected to bring about a major transformation. WAP appeared to promise major gains as it was backed by the three big telecommunication equipment manufacturers at the time, namely Ericsson, Nokia and Motorola, along with Unwired Planet. However, somewhere along the way, it has lost some of its promise. According to some estimates, only 10 per cent of all GSM phones use WAP and its promise of becoming the de facto standard has not been realized. In contrast, NTT DOCOMO's iMode, which developed a language called C-HTML, is a success.

The entry of Microsoft into this space forced established companies like Nokia, which were till then reluctant to open up their phones to development, to change their position. Symbian/EPOC operating systems, Nokia and others soon began to allow third-party development and, in the bargain, spawned many communities.

Superior number crunching capability has enabled modern smart phones to implement complex encryption and security algorithms. Leveraging this capability and coupled with medium- to high-speed Internet access, it was now possible to introduce virtual financial transactions.

Over the past decade, RFID technology has matured around two main players – Philips (now NXP) and Sony. Sony's FeliCa and Philips' MIFARE were the two dominant technologies worldwide, and RFID (radio frequency identification) technology was bound to find its way to the phone. With phones as an individual's always-on ubiquitous device, it was ideally suited for all proximity RFID applications such as bus and train ticketing, and stored-value cards.

Sony, Philips and Nokia set up the NFC standard, which allows proximity transactions between mobile phones and fixed terminals such as ticket turnstiles and point-of-sale terminals.

With NFC, entry/exit to and from stations and buses could now be facilitated by simply waving or tapping the phone in front of the terminal.

In parallel, the smart card technology kept maturing and finding its way into key applications. The smart card, by virtue of its inherent high security, has a number of applications, including the next generation of credit cards (replacing the magnetic swipe card), health cards, driving licences and even e-passports.

Smart card and NFC technologies are being amalgamated into the smart phone. The NFC-smart card combination in a phone will enable credit card transactions as the user waves the phone in front of a terminal – thus ensuring that the 'credit card' does not even leave the user's hand as the transaction is completed. It is easy to see that credit cards, prepaid cards, loyalty cards, e-passport, tickets, coupons, etc. will now be embedded into the smart phone and that proximity transactions will be through a gentle tap or perhaps just a wave of the phone.

The mobile digital wallet, predicted as far back as in 1994 – long before the advent of mobile phones – has become a reality and is offered as a third-party application for most phones. It facilitates mobile banking, bill payment, virtual transactions as well as real-world proximity transactions – all from the latest technology marvel called the smart phone. Money has truly gone mobile!

Of course, while all this was going on, sexier features such as camera phones, both still and video, with ever increasing resolution, were also being introduced. But such was the stereotype of phones being primarily a carrier of voice, that back in 1999, when Microsoft chairman and CEO Bill Gates demonstrated a prototype of a Windows CE-based smart phone capable of accessing the Internet, many people were not sure about the eventual potential of the technology.

Over the last several years, the number of smart phones has grown significantly, and even though that number is still a small fraction of the total number of mobile phones in the world, there are clear indications that in the next five to ten years, all mobile phone users will carry smart phones.

SMART PHONE

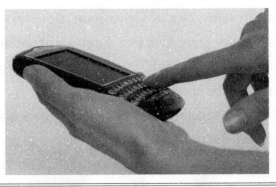

Smart phones go beyond regular mobile phones in their ability to run a complete operating system software that provides a standardized interface and platform for application developers. Unlike the PDA-based devices of the past, which ran on touch-screen and pen approach, smart phones use a standard phone keypad for input. They come equipped with much more powerful processors and bigger displays. Compared to Java or BREW applications, native smart phone applications usually run faster on smart phones. They also integrate better with phone hardware.

All these features make smart phones capable of being an effective alternative to PCs and laptops for all practical purposes. One of the deciding factors for the widespread adoption of smart phones will be their price, which is still in the range of several hundred dollars. The price is certainly an inhibiting factor but industry analysts expect it to go down significantly in the next one or two years.

The block diagrams on pages 123-25 exhibit the fundamental building blocks of smart phones – providing functional, hardware and software perspectives. Functionally, smart phones consist of the basic telephony components related to voice and data, various hardware resources, the operating system and programming capabilities similar to personal computers, and the ability to support various applications and utilities. From a hardware perspective, in addition to the basic voice and data connectivity capabilities,

smart phones are characterized by different input and output capabilities, including touch-sensitive screens, support for different proximity communication protocols over infrared and RF, and modules like cameras and fingerprint sensors to facilitate value-added services. From a software perspective, as outlined in the diagram, smart phones support web browsing, productivity and enterprise applications, multimedia and entertainment services, and increasingly, support for third party or non-handset manufacturer applications built to operate on the phone's operating system.

SMART PHONE BLOCK DIAGRAMS

SMART PHONE Functional Snapshot

Smart Phone

Hardware Resources

- Input
  - Keyboard
  - Stylus
- Display
  - Colour LCD
  - Touch Screen
- Data Connectivity
  - Remote
    - GPRS/CDMA
    - 3G/EDGE
    - USSD
  - Local
    - Wired
      - Serial/USB-OTG
    - Wireless
      - Infra-red
      - Bluetooth
      - WiFi
      - WIMAX
      - NFC
- Camera
  - 2-5 Megapixel
  - Digital Zoom
  - Auto Recording
  - Video Recording
- Power Management
  - Battery
  - Charger
  - Vibrator
- Multimedia
  - Media Player
  - FM Stereo Radio
  - Ring Tones
  - Video Streaming

Basic Phone Functionality

- Voice
  - Microphone
  - Headset
  - Speaker
  - Hands Free
  - Recorder
- Messaging
  - SMS
    - Dictionary
    - Multilingual
    - Storage
    - Picture

Applications & Utilities

- Applications
  - Productivity
    - Contacts
    - Calendar
    - To Do List
    - Calculator
    - Notes
    - Appointments
    - Scheduler
    - Clock
  - Professional
    - Word Documents
    - Excel Spreadsheets
    - pdf Reader
    - e-books
  - Entertainment
    - Games
    - Media Player
    - Gallery
    - Content
- Digital Services
  - Wall Papers
  - Screen Savers
  - Themes
  - Ring Tones
  - Games
  - Filmware Updates
- Call Management
  - Logs
  - Speed Dialling
  - Call Wait, Hold, Divert
  - Conference
  - Voice Mail
- Browsing
  - WAP
  - Internet

Operating System & Programming

- Programming Language
  - C, C++
  - J2ME
  - Python
  - BREW
- Operating System
  - Symbian
  - Windows
  - Linux
  - Android

SMART PHONE
Hardware Components

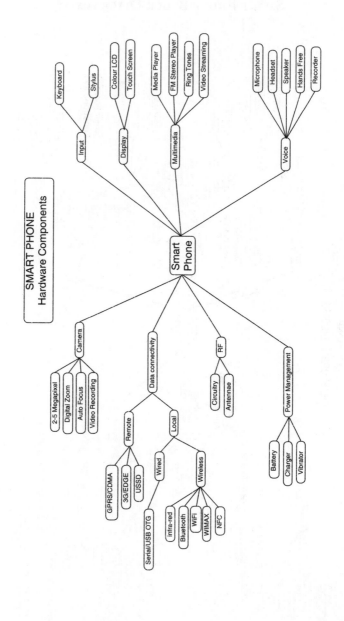

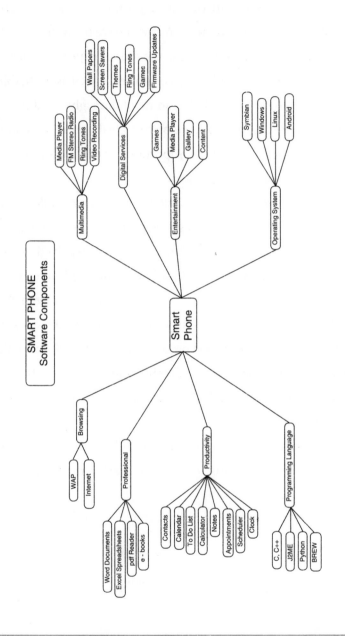

SMART PHONE
Software Components

Smart Phone

- Browsing
  - WAP
  - Internet
- Professional
  - Word Documents
  - Excel Spreadsheets
  - pdf Reader
  - e - books
- Productivity
  - Contacts
  - Calendar
  - To Do List
  - Calculator
  - Notes
  - Appointments
  - Scheduler
  - Clock
- Programming Language
  - C, C++
  - J2ME
  - Python
  - BREW
- Multimedia
  - Media Player
  - FM Stereo Radio
  - Ring Tones
  - Video Recording
- Digital Services
  - Wall Papers
  - Screen Savers
  - Themes
  - Ring Tones
  - Games
  - Firmware Updates
- Entertainment
  - Games
  - Media Player
  - Gallery
  - Content
- Operating System
  - Symbian
  - Windows
  - Linux
  - Android

As the population of smart phone grows, telecom companies, banks and merchants will have to come up with features and services that make the mobile experience richer and more convenient for the consumer as well as profitable for themselves. To think that some of the higher-end smart phones are equipped to store up to 2 gigabytes reveals how powerful they are and how important it is to make optimum use of their processing power.

If the growth of mobile telephony is any guide, then the spread of smart phones is expected to be a matter of months rather than years. That in turn will drive the demand for features, functionalities, services and applications on the mobile phone. Quite predictably, Japan has been the trendsetter in terms of early adaptation of advances in mobile telephony, including its acceptance of the mobile wallet, which uses a host of technologies such as infrared, contactless RF chips, SMS, interactive voice response and mobile scan.

The story of smart phones is full of fascinating, if sometimes disastrous, efforts to chart a new world of telecommunications.

8

The Mobile Wallet

The genesis of the technology that eventually led to mobile payments predates the emergence of smart phones, although it had to wait for the advent of smart phones to acquire the kind of popular traction it has in the past several years. Some two decades after the invention of the electronic or digital diary in 1975, which, as it turned out, was among the earliest precursors to personal digital assistants, or PDAs, and eventually, smart phones, it was a domestic situation in Chicago that triggered the concept of the digital wallet (see Preface)!

The electronic diary essentially digitized the ubiquitous paper diary most of us used to carry around, in which we stored names, addresses, phone numbers, appointments, and other important personal information. The digital diary not only digitized all of this, with simple user access through a touch-sensitive liquid crystal display, but also linked events to alerts, and essentially set the stage for smart applications, or applications that come to the user as opposed to the user going to a specific application.

Similarly, in its most simplistic form, the digital wallet digitized all the key components of the leather wallet, which fundamentally consists of an empty jacket, a plethora of plastic and paper cards, coupons, bills, receipts, photographs, and cash. The inventor (Sam Pitroda) professed that a digital wallet would consist of a liquid crystal display not much bigger than a regular plastic bank card, with preferably a touch-sensitive screen and simple user interface that lets the user flip through the digital wallet in the same manner she/he flips through a leather wallet. This would give the user the ability to receive over-the-air various cards, coupons, bills, etc. in electronic form, preserving the branding and image of such tokens, which are paramount for user recognition and consequently adoption, as well as for the service providers who have spent billions of dollars creating their brands. This digital wallet could be used to beam a card at a point of sale as opposed to handing over a piece of plastic, and the receipt could be beamed back to the digital wallet, which could be signed, stored and archived.

128

In a patent filed in the US in 1994, Pitroda outlined in great detail the user interface: how the user could load and flip through multiple cards; how banks and other service providers could issue their respective cards and tokens securely over-the-air using existing wired or wireless networks; how users could beam their cards and tokens using radio frequency or infrared or bar codes into point-of-sale terminals or remote service providers; how these in turn would possibly need special adapters to accept such beamed cards and tokens and beam receipts back to the user's digital wallet; how consumers could store and archive receipts; and how such a system would support not only payment and financial services but also various other applications related to insurance, health, etc.

Even in 1994, when the concept of smart mobile phones was non-existent, it was clear that with the processing power of computer chips doubling every year, it would not be long before mobile phones would begin to rival the power of PCs. At the same time, it was obvious that plastic credit cards were reaching their optimal use and had to be re-engineered to bring them in line with the digital age. As with the electronic or digital diary, which became quite popular in the 1980s because it offered functionalities that people found very user friendly, secure and convenient, it was important that any advance in digitizing plastic credit cards had to incorporate ease of use and security.

From the standpoint of eventually commercializing such a technology, it was equally important that image and branding, something credit card companies were so particular about, were an integral part of the idea. Without the image and branding, a digital wallet would lose much of its appeal for the credit card issuers. Also, the user interface had to be simple and intuitive. In order to achieve that, the digital wallet had to have the look and feel of a leather wallet in terms of credit card images and so on. Storing images on a digital device would not only make the transition from a leather to a digital wallet a smooth affair for the consumers but also incentivize credit card issuers to graduate from plastic to digital without losing their visual recognition and brand loyalty. American Express would definitely want to show its centurion on a digital wallet, as would MasterCard show its two circles, and Visa its three stripes.

In addition to storing tokens and conducting transactions, the digital wallet would also need the ability to store receipts. It was a logical next step in a device that would allow people to spend. If one spends, it makes sense to have the ability to store and manage receipts. Yet another feature was built in keeping in mind the requirements of potential corporate users of such a digital wallet. That feature was the ability to manage and file expense reports from the device. Most of us who travel on business have invariably lost out on reimbursements because of the small thermal paper receipts taxi drivers continue to use. Imagine the advantages of not only paying with your digital wallet without worrying about carrying cards, but more importantly, getting an electronic receipt that can immediately be tagged as a business expense, and electronically filed along with other expenses for reimbursement. The tax authorities could easily justify the additional infrastructure and standardization to drive such a system that extended beyond just business expenses to all payments, if only to make their own auditing easier and efficient.

The ability of the digital wallet to generate, store and archive receipts or electronic records cannot be emphasized enough. Consumers and businesses spend significant amounts of time and resources towards capturing, storing, and analyzing receipts. Similarly, regulators in particular and governments in general are continuously trying to figure out better means of collecting and authenticating receipts for reporting and auditing purposes.

An even bigger task is analyzing these stored receipts – to enable better planning and budgeting in a household or enterprise; to personalize products and services for customers; to generate usage patterns and identify fraud in real time for financial institutions. Akin to electronic discovery and management of digital documents largely for judicial requirements, there is a tremendous business potential in just archiving, managing, and analyzing digital receipts.

Hence the digital wallet's ability to instantaneously create, store, and archive a digital receipt impacts all of the above. As much as good progress has been made on standardizing electronic records or digital receipts, there is still some way to go before electronic records will have the same level of legality as paper receipts. Nevertheless, the promise of getting a digital receipt as the transaction is completed is an important one, with significant implications for consumers, enterprises, and regulators.

The first patent covering the concept of the digital wallet was filed in the US in 1994 and issued in 1996, with regional filings in several other countries, including Japan and Europe. The invention made the implicit assumption that consumers would either go to a store, buy an empty digital wallet and then stuff it with cards, coupons and other tokens in a similar fashion as their leather wallets, or they would buy a mobile phone, sign up with their carrier of choice, and then go to either their carrier, bank or other service provider to securely download over-the-air a software version of the digital wallet.

Once this empty software jacket is set up on the mobile phone, or possibly pre-loaded by the handset manufacturer, then just as in the digital wallet, the user would load this mobile wallet with electronic replicas of cards and other tokens, to subsequently conduct transactions, store receipts

and avail of value-added services, all through a single, secure, and simple interface on the mobile phone.

Effectively, the invention of the digital diary in 1975, which led to the invention of the digital wallet in 1994, laid the foundation for the mobile wallet. And while the term mobile wallet is in vogue now, as we will see over the course of this chapter, it means different things to different stakeholders – ranging from a simple and secure repository of strictly payment instruments to an elaborate aggregation of tokens, applications, and value-added services on a mobile phone.

The figure on the following page outlines the evolution of secure transaction services through the mobile phone, where the first step is to use the phone for conducting remote or over-the-air transactions such as paying bills, topping up airtime, banking, etc. The next step is to go beyond payments to other value-added services over-the-air, such as ticketing and coupons, and eventually using the mobile phone for both remote as well as proximity transactions leveraging the Near Field Communication or NFC-based infrastructure and true cash replacement.

EVOLUTION OF MOBILE TRANSACTION SERVICES

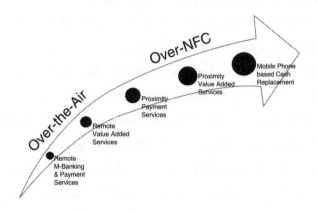

As much as the terms m-purse, m-banking, m-ticketing, m-money transfer, m-advertising, and m-commerce are gaining rapid popularity and recognition, a true leather wallet metaphor continues to be elusive on the mobile phone. We have chronicled (and continue to witness) several experiments of using mobile phones for conducting payments, but have yet to see mass adoption of a true leather wallet metaphor on the mobile.

To qualify the above statement, what we mean by a true leather wallet metaphor is this: the ability as a consumer to go out and procure an empty leather wallet of choice; to personalize this leather wallet with photographs and other sentimental incidentals; to stuff cash; to arrange a plethora of cards from various banks, airlines, insurance companies and others in preferential order; to stuff coupons and bills from various merchants, service providers, utilities and others in preferential order; to conduct transactions; and to store and archive receipts – all of this in an extremely simple and intuitive manner.

MOBILE WALLET USER INTERFACE

Now if we were to define our (ideal) mobile wallet, as a consumer we would want the facility to do all of the above. The figure below outlines some of the services a consumer will want from her/his mobile wallet, to seamlessly conduct secure transactions in the real and virtual world.

135

MOBILE WALLET SERVICES

BANKING	BILL PAYMENTS	MONEY TRANSFER	INSURANCE
P2P PAYMENTS	MICRO-CREDIT & FINANCE	NFC / PROXIMITY	PREPAID TOP-UP
TICKETING	COUPONS & LOYALTY	ADVERTISING	SHOPPING & GIFT CARDS

Additionally, as consumers we would also want our mobile wallet to have capabilities related to secure over-the-air transactions; various value-added and matching services based on our static as well as dynamic profiles; the ability to manage throughput of and intelligently prioritize personalized transactions; and smart content and smart applications, where the personalized content and secure applications come to us as opposed to requiring us to go to different services to perform routine tasks.

If the above defines a mobile wallet, it is safe to state that we have yet to see a credible (mobile) successor to the ubiquitous leather wallet.

The above definition outlines the user perspective of what a mobile wallet or a digital wallet should look like. From the perspective of the providers, which include all the banks, carriers, utilities, merchants, service providers, or token issuers and acquirers for cards, coupons, bills, etc., the following will be required: the ability to securely issue their respective tokens remotely or wirelessly over-the-air, along with the branding and imagery as well as the credentials to facilitate the transactions; the ability to transfer their existing risk management practices to this new mobile channel and environment; the ability to aggregate various services as part of their existing cross-selling and co-branding initiatives; the ability to acquire all of these transactions preferably over existing settlement networks; the ability to leverage their existing reporting, auditing and campaign management systems on the back end; and all of this without any disintermediation of their existing customer acquisition and customer support channels.

When it comes to the mobile wallet, service providers, like users, will want to leverage the advances in information and communication technologies, specifically in the areas of security, biometric authentication, fraud prevention, pattern recognition, profiling, matching services, redundancy, disaster recovery, business continuity, distributed infrastructure, and further optimization through virtualization.

To ensure that billions of users worldwide can recreate their existing leather wallet metaphor on their mobile phones, what is required is not a stand-alone product or service but rather a highly robust and secure web-service-

137

based transaction platform that has the ability to securely interconnect – on the back end with existing token issuers, acquirers, service provider host systems and related settlement networks; and on the front end reach out to users first to issue an empty leather wallet metaphor or software jacket, which can then be populated by various providers with electronic equivalents of their plastic and paper tokens, similar to the leather wallet. Once populated with these tokens – cards, coupons, bills, etc. – the user should be able to securely conduct transactions in the real world over NFC by tapping or waving her/his mobile phone at existing point-of-sale locations, as well as remotely over-the-air in the virtual world. The user should be able to store electronic receipts of such transactions and avail of various profile-driven, value-added and matching services.

To ensure that the mobile wallet truly becomes a repository of digital tokens, providing the user access to various secure transactions and value-added services, the platform will have to bring together all the stakeholders, and effectively leverage the existing connectivity as well as settlement infrastructure. The figure below outlines the ecosystem that will be required to support the mobile wallet for the user.

For example, if the user has fifty different cards, coupons, bills, etc. in her/his leather wallet, she/he will expect nothing less in the mobile wallet. Aside from preserving the branding and user interfaces, which include the ability to flip through different tokens and rearrange them in a preferential order, what this means is that the above platform will have to support fifty-plus-one different security schemes, so that every individual service provider, along with the provider of the empty leather wallet jacket or software, can implement their preferred security scheme directly with the end user, without any disintermediation.

As different markets will have different delivery and business models, such a platform will have to support configurability of different trust models to facilitate the above security requirements, as providers can secure various vulnerability points from the user's device or mobile phone, across the different wireless and wired networks and service provider domains, and eventually back to the provider's host transaction system and settlement network. Beyond securing these vulnerability points, the platform will also have to ensure that the existing risk management practices evolved over years by the service providers, on a stand-alone basis as well as through aggregation, can be effectively transferred to the mobile channel.

Hundreds of millions of people around the world have a lot riding on credit cards in terms of their sensitive personal information. In a country like the US, where credit cards are used extensively, they offer an explicit peek into the life of its user, unlike cash, which leaves no paper trail. Related to

139

MOBILE WALLET ECOSYSTEM

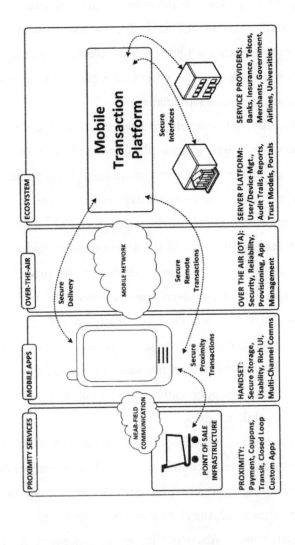

credit cards is information such as the user's social security number, which is the most important piece of identity those living in the US can possibly have.

Hence it is imperative that the mobile wallet's security is simple and adequate to ensure that the consumer or user is comfortable; and that it is also impenetrable and robust enough for the providers to deploy and scale. It is clear that several layers of security would be required, including device- and transmission-level security, and infrastructure or server-side security.

Device-level security would ensure that the personal and other sensitive user information is securely stored in an encrypted database inside the device or on a back end server, which in turn could only be accessed by an authenticated user, device and domain. Access to this encrypted information would have to be facilitated by credentials that only the user is aware of, which could include biometric identifiers such as finger prints, retinal scans or voice, along with the device's unique identifier, and the domain's identifier. The security industry now has well-standardized solutions for multi-factor authentication, which could be modified and extended to the mobile device and channel at large, and more importantly, configured to support the extensive trust models that will be required to support the underlying business and delivery models.

141

Transmission security would ensure that all the data sent from the device to the back end host is encrypted, which would most definitely leverage application layer security schemes in addition to transport layer security provided by the bearer networks, possibly leveraging a wireless public key infrastructure (w/PKI)-based schema. Every time data is transmitted from the user to the service provider or vice versa, it would have to be encoded; similarly, decoding this information would require keys, which could be shared between the user and the service providers but at the same time be stored and transmitted in such a way that it cannot be tapped by someone sitting in the middle. Similarly, data that is transmitted to the NFC-powered point-of-sale terminal would have to be encrypted using a PKI-based system shared between the issuers, acquirers and other supporting entities in the entire issuance and settlement process.

The science of securing the back end infrastructure or host environment is fairly well-standardized and perfected, with elaborate DMZ or demilitarized zones protecting the entry point of such domains or networks, and supported by elaborate firewalls, security utilities, processes, compliance and auditing to ensure that it becomes extremely difficult, if not impossible, to breach.

As security experts, or, for that matter anyone, relatively well versed with physical security schemes and encryption would state, there is no such thing as a system that is

142

impossible to breach; mathematically, with infinite time or infinite computing power, any crypto (a way to scramble information so that it cannot be easily cracked or opened), which is the cornerstone of all security systems, can be broken and effectively used to compromise the larger system architecture. What this means in practical terms is that since one does not have the liberty of infinite time, all one needs is access to significant processing capability, so that as this capability increases, the time to crack the crypto effectively decreases.

Moving beyond the mathematical complexities of security and related algorithms, which is not only a science by itself but also a global industry, the implications on mobile wallets, and specifically the supporting platform, is that it will have to provide not only an extremely high level of sophistication in terms of the security architecture, but perhaps more importantly, enable the service providers to leverage their existing risk management models perfected for other comparable channels for the mobile wallet.

In some ways, this particular requirement of leveraging existing risk management models, which is intrinsically related to the security architecture and managing multiple trust models, is the most challenging aspect of the mobile wallet, which, in its native leather wallet form, enables different service providers to maintain (an almost) perfect one-to-one relation with their customer.

143

It is critical that the mobile wallet provides multiple payment options, as consumers do not always make payments with a single instrument, be it a credit card, debit card or a bank account. And it is imperative that the platform for mobile wallets supports aggregation and multiple trust models that can be dynamically configured. Users will always demand options, and hence the mobile wallet and its supporting platform will have to ensure a high level of configurability, flexibility, and aggregation.

Hence, beyond the user interface, branding, over-the-air issuance, transaction capability, and receipt storage, the most critical elements will be the platform's ability of aggregating multiple tokens, without disintermediation between the provider and the consumer, and enabling the provider to seamlessly transfer existing risk models to the mobile channel.

The figure below reiterates the above, stressing the importance of how the mobile wallet will need to be consumer-centric as opposed to provider-centric as early experiments have proven to be, and how it will have to support multiple tokens – cards, coupons, bills, etc. – and multiple services coming from multiple providers. The figure also outlines some of the fundamental building blocks of the secure web-service-based platform that will be required to support the mobile wallet. These would range from ensuring that a consumer with a broken or stolen phone can immediately report the loss of the device and also get a new version of her/his mobile wallet reloaded on a new device, with the platform locking up the old version of the mobile wallet and replicating a new version on the new device, to providing profile-driven matching and value-added services based on analysis of various static as well as dynamic inputs related to the users and their respective transaction history.

PLATFORM BUILDING BLOCKS

WALLET METAPHOR WITH BRANDING	MULTIPLE CARDS & SERVICES	USER-CENTRIC INTERFACE & SMART APPLICATIONS
OVER-THE-AIR ISSUANCE	SECURITY & RISK MANAGEMENT	TRUST MODELS & AGGREGATION
VIRTUAL & REAL WORLD TRANSACTIONS	RECEIPT STORAGE & MANAGEMENT	PROFILE BASED VALUE ADDED & MATCHING SERVICES

As the patents filed with the US patent office in 1994 (USPTO# 5,590,038) and 1996 (USPTO# 5,884,271) outlined the digital or mobile wallet from a user's perspective, a patent filed in 1999 (USPTO# 7,308,426) and issued in 2007 by the USPTO outlines the ecosystem and landscape from a platform's perspective, detailing how such a platform will have to manage multiple users, devices and domains. The inventor (Sam Pitroda) professed that as the adoption of digital wallets grows, either through mobile phones or any other medium, the role of this platform will continue to evolve, from issuing tokens and facilitating transactions to creating rich profiles of users and service providers based on their static, dynamic, and usage-based inputs. And from matching users with products and services from providers based on these different variables to providing profile-driven, value-added services related to applications and incentives. The patent further outlined the expert system that would power such a platform and ensure it scales as millions of users start to conduct transactions, requiring the platform to manage and analyse a large amount of data related to the user as well as the provider.

Based on recent trends, such a platform will need to support multiple delivery models to sustain different business models across different markets – both in terms of regions as well as demographics. The mobile wallet could be delivered as SaaS or Software-as-a-Service, or through an ASP or Application Service Provider, or by a large infrastructure provider such as Carrier or by a bank or a merchant through their hosted applications and services.

Additionally, such a platform will also have to support tools and utilities, which in turn will enable a community of developers to build its own solutions without really worrying about issues related to the channel/s, transaction management, security, and smart application management. It is imperative that the platform hide all the complexity related to managing the channel, as well as managing the secure and personalized transactions 'under-the-hood', enabling the actual business drivers to directly define, build and distribute their respective solutions, based on their preferred business model and leveraging the most optimal delivery model, both of which can be configured to support local requirements using a global platform.

From a service provider's perspective, this platform will have to enable it to save costs related to its existing services, generate revenues from new services and solutions, and acquire new customers, not always in the same order, as each provider will have its own priorities.

As an example, a bank could leverage the growing number of mobile phone users to not only acquire new banking customers, but also save costs incurred in their lobbies and call centres by moving the relevant repetitive enquiries and services to this secure mobile channel, and generate revenues by aggregating non-banking services like coupons, gift cards and stored value.

Similarly, merchants, who already capture and analyze a lot of data related to their customers and their buying patterns, could now use the growing mobile channel to extend their existing campaign management systems and profiling systems. They could issue electronic coupons, gift cards, and stored-value cards securely and directly over-the-air into their customer's mobile wallet. The consumer could wave or tap the phone at an NFC-powered point-of-sale system, and, in a single tap, complete the payment, redeem a coupon and update loyalty. This would help merchants move a lot more customers through their check-out lanes at peak periods, consequently increasing their revenues and directly adding to their bottom line.

It is estimated that more than a billion paper coupons are redeemed in the US alone every year, so possibly trillions of paper coupons are issued every year. Even if a fraction of these coupons is issued in electronic form over-the-air directly to a user's mobile wallet, imagine the cost savings on the issuance and settlement related to these paper coupons alone.

Based on the notion that costs related to producing, delivering and supporting products and services are always passed on to the consumer, and if the contrary were applicable (though we cannot guarantee the same), such costs savings should definitely lead to the savings being passed on to the consumers either in the form of discounts and rebates, or through lower costs of goods and services.

It is not inconceivable that as such a platform evolves, the personalized content, transactions and solutions this platform powers for mobile phone users will also be accessed through other channels. Effectively, commuters could start paying their bills using their mobile phone on the train, and as the commuter's station arrives, she/he could complete paying the balance bills at home, using an iteration of the same mobile wallet loaded on their set-top-box-powered television set.

It is also not inconceivable that as such a platform evolves, it will also power other non-financial services, such as those related to health or education or governance, which are sensitive to issues related to the user interface, branding, security, risk management, disintermediation, business model, delivery model, customer acquisition and customer support.

Similar to a credit card issued over-the-air securely to a mobile wallet, such a platform will be required to issue a patient's clinical data securely over-the-air to the health provider's mobile phone, enabling the provider to examine the data and prescribe follow-up in real time, which could involve sending a prescription securely over-the-air to the pharmacy, finally allowing the patient to pay for the prescription using the mobile wallet, either over-the-air or in proximity to the pharmacy.

Hence, to offer a true leather wallet metaphor on mobile phones to consumers, service providers will have to deploy a secure web-service-based transaction platform, which will not only recreate the metaphor but also aggregate various

149

tokens and services. It will have the intelligence to deliver smart content and smart applications, the ability to support services beyond payments, and will be able to scale to channels beyond the mobile phone.

Telecom companies, in particular, due to their ownership of various communication channels, be it over mobile phones or PCs or IPTV, are in an ideal position to host and manage a secure transaction platform that complements existing content management platforms. At the back end, this platform will securely integrate with existing content providers, payment and settlement providers, and service providers, and at the front end, it will reach out to consumers over various channels to provide a pervasive and user-friendly interface for accessing content, incentives, and conducting secure transactions. The figure below outlines some of the key factors related to usability, service provisioning and aggregation, which will be necessary to ensure that the mobile wallet can be accessed across multiple channels, and be effectively deployed, scaled and sustained.

For the large part, the technology to offer various services as point-solutions exists now, and by that we mean that the infrastructure is in place, new technologies and platforms have been field-tested, and relevant standards have been agreed upon. In lieu of this, telecom companies, banks, and merchants have launched, and continue to scale, albeit not that successfully, their individual offerings.

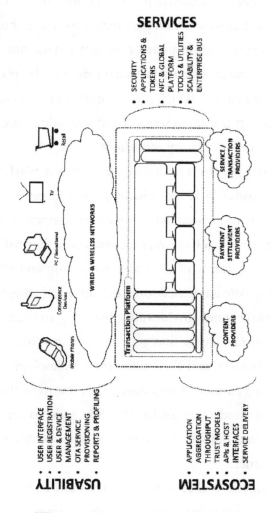

SERVICES

- SECURITY
- APPLICATIONS & TOKENS
- NFC & GLOBAL PLATFORM
- TOOLS & UTILITIES
- SCALABILITY & ENTERPRISE BUS

Retail

TV

PC / Broadband

Convergence Devices

Mobile Phones

WIRED & WIRELESS NETWORKS

SERVICE / TRANSACTION PROVIDERS

PAYMENT / SETTLEMENT PROVIDERS

CONTENT PROVIDERS

Transaction Platform

USABILITY
- USER INTERFACE
- USER REGISTRATION
- USER & DEVICE MANAGEMENT
- OTA SERVICE PROVISIONING
- REPORTS & PROFILING

ECOSYSTEM
- APPLICATION
- AGGREGATION
- THROUGHPUT
- TRUST MODELS
- APIs & HOST INTERFACES
- SERVICE DELIVERY

From a consumer's perspective, real value will be delivered when they can, through a single and simple interface on their mobile phone, avail themselves of all transactional services for payment as well as non-payment applications, bundled with the appropriate amount of content and incentives. To enable this, the providers will need the right kind of platform as described earlier, which can not only optimize usability and efficiently provision services, but also help create, scale and sustain the necessary ecosystem.

As much as the technology for such a platform is available today, a bigger challenge lies in terms of the underlying business model, for telecom companies, banks, and merchants will have to agree upon how they will share the upside in terms of customer acquisition and revenue generation. We have used some examples to highlight that the mobile channel provides an opportunity to acquire new customers, save costs, and generate new revenues for all the stakeholders, and their supporting technology as well as operating partners. Consequently, if done right, there is a significant upside, provided all the three stakeholders come together, without which true value will not be delivered to the consumer.

The mobile wallet will allow telecom companies to generate issuance-based revenues for various tokens and services provided by the banks and merchants, and both the

banks and merchants will start to recognize the cost savings associated with the channel. As the customer acquisition starts to pick up, banks and merchants could share some of the cost savings related to acquiring new customers with telecom companies, as they help share the cost of distributing, marketing and educating consumers on these new services offered by the banks and merchants. As usage starts to pick up, and all the stakeholders develop a better sense of how the mobile wallet will positively impact the overall risk related to provisioning various services and settling transactions, all three stakeholders could further share potential costs savings related to fraud and identity theft.

Beyond customer acquisition and costs savings, the mobile wallet will provide all the three stakeholders opportunities to generate new revenue streams by cross-selling and co-branding services. The only sustainable business model is where telecom companies, banks and merchants work together to deliver true value to consumers, and effectively share the costs saved and new revenues generated.

The rise of the mobile wallet intrinsically means the rise of mobile money; we are on the threshold of a historic shift in the way we perceive, produce and spend money. We do not have to look beyond our existing leather wallet to truly understand what will make up a mobile wallet, but like a lot of other things in life, what is obvious and simple as a concept is also deceivingly complex to deliver and scale. The mobile wallet continues to be elusive, possibly because the complexities of such a platform are yet to be simplified to an extent that all stakeholders can truly leverage it, or because it just hasn't been embraced by consumers and providers yet.

Whether it is the evolution of cards (smart cards to contactless cards), or the electronic diary (digital wallet to the mobile wallet), recent trends lead us to state that the mobile wallet – or the true replication of the leather wallet metaphor on mobile phones – will become ubiquitous sooner rather than later, and when that does happen, it will bring about profound changes in the way service providers interact with each other as well as with consumers, providing an opportunity for consumers to leverage this capability to make radical changes to their overall lifestyle.

It is safe to state that the mobile wallet will lead to mobilization of money in ways the world has never witnessed before. Similar to other disruptive technologies, a lot will depend on how we as humans leverage this profound capability – to uplift society at large or hasten its downfall.

9

Lifestyle: Pipe, Fund and Provider

There is a slow tectonic shift waiting to occur underneath the banking world due to the emergence of the mobile Internet, which will eventually alter the concept of banking, payment and money. With over half of the world's population connected via mobile phones already, this is bound to have far-reaching implications on social, economic and cultural life the world over. Carriers worldwide have invested enormous amounts of resources and capital to create mobile networks and services. Hardly a week goes by without a major announcement in the media about new mobile applications, opportunities, alliances and upgrades. With mobile phones becoming smarter and more powerful, with colour displays and cameras, we essentially get a personal computer on the phone and Internet on the move with limitless possibilities.

Over the past several chapters we have tried to chronicle the evolution of telecommunication, both in terms of underlying technologies as well as entities that have pushed the envelope and set trends over the years. Today, telecommunication is no longer just about access. What started with government agencies providing wired, and later wireless, access for consumers and service providers has evolved over the years into a strong and, in many cases, private enterprise no longer limited to providing mere connectivity between end-points.

The archaic and monopolistic agencies of yore have been largely privatized and revamped, providing wired, wireless and broadband-based services, with highly specialized offerings for different segments of the consumer market, as well as different bundled packages and services for enterprises across the spectrum, from small- and medium-size businesses to large global multinationals.

With the explosive growth of the Internet and thriving global community of online service providers, combined with the exponential adoption of mobile phones and continuous expansion of the underlying wireless infrastructure, the focus is now largely on providing more bandwidth over wired and wireless networks.

Today most consumers, in addition to making voice calls, sending short messages, and downloading ring tones, expect to be able to check their email, local weather and traffic, while on the go. When the term smart phone was first introduced, it referred to a mobile phone with a touch-sensitive screen that was also a personal digital assistant. Today, the only difference between a regular mobile phone and smart phone appears to be that the former is meant for consumers while the latter caters to enterprises, but even that distinction is gradually disappearing.

Similarly, there is no enterprise knowledge worker who does not carry a mobile phone, some specialized device for emails and messaging, and a laptop equipped with wireless broadband connectivity. While this has definitely increased overall productivity, it also highlights blurring lines between work and personal time, with self-help books advising workers on how to resist the urge of sleeping with their BlackBerrys.

With consumers and enterprises relying increasingly on data-driven services, telecommunication companies have already made, and continue to make, significant investments in their infrastructure to handle higher and higher amounts of bandwidth. The phrase 'build it and they will come' could not be more apt, with a new-found service coming up every other day.

Now even voice services, which were analogue in nature

compared to data services, which are digital, are available over IP- or Internet protocol-driven data-based networks. VoIP or Voice-over IP solutions, which initially started small, focusing on PC-to-PC-based communication, are now available over mobile phones. The next generation wireless infrastructure promises to provide VoIP as a standard capability, increasing the possibility of voice being completely free for consumers while the telecom companies' entire business model is driven purely by data-based services.

At the other extreme is a new service that provides consumers with regular television programming over the Internet as a data service. As one can imagine, if this service truly becomes popular with consumers, it will hog tremendous amounts of bandwidth from the networks. Irrespective of the outcome of this particular service, it is safe to say that our consumption of data from the networks will continue to grow unabated.

Telecommunication companies have recognized this thirst for data, and many of them see themselves as the gatekeepers of these pipes. A recent spectrum auction in the United States attracted a lot of attention for the simple fact that it was billed as a fight between the evil empire comprising existing telecommunication companies that want to control and put a price on access, and the New Age Internet companies touted as the saviours of the common man, demanding open and free access for all.

Mildly put, both positions were highly exaggerated, but the auction has sparked an interesting debate on how telecommunication companies should function and innovate around not only products and services but also different business models in this increasingly connected world. Though the highly anticipated battle of good versus evil fizzled out, the fact does remain that telecommunication companies are now increasingly being forced to transform themselves from just a pipe into a 'lifestyle management pipe'.

With this opportunity also comes higher pressure to differentiate and to generate higher average revenue per user (ARPU) or profitability. Building these networks is not cheap, and if someone were to truly take the cost of this infrastructure worldwide, it would easily go into several trillions of dollars. Hence, while it is difficult to argue against the position taken by the telecommunication companies, open and free access not only spurs on creativity at an individual level and profitability at an enterprise level, it could also turn out to be the lifeline for the bulk of humanity that struggles at the bottom of the pyramid.

As both arguments seem valid and well-placed, the solution could very well be in telecom companies providing more than just connectivity. If they were to truly become a lifestyle management pipe, consumers might start seeing the value in paying for value-added services that enhance their overall lifestyle rather than just provide access.

Similar to the telecommunication industry, the banking industry has also evolved over the years, both in terms of technologies as well as entities that have become trend-setters, forcing others to adapt to the growing demands of consumers and enterprise. Just as telecommunication companies are rightly labelled as the infrastructure to the infrastructure, banking is the engine that enables the masses to create and manage wealth at an individual level; leverage credit, manage risk and drive profitability at an enterprise level; and generate higher GDP at a national level.

Gone are the days when banking was limited to a small community, where people could safely deposit their funds and expect loans when they needed to build a home or start a business. As much as the fundamentals have not changed, global banking, which the traditionalist could well argue to be an oxymoron, is far more diverse and complex.

The banking industry the world over has invested heavily and benefited substantially from computer technology to evolve traditional services related to chequing, saving, loans, debts, credit cards, etc. Banks first focused on computer applications in back offices to improve productivity, efficiency, and reduce cost. They then moved on to front offices for tellers to improve customer services. Similarly, banks have also invested heavily over the last twenty-five years to create a global ATM infrastructure to improve access and take some of the banking services to street corners. Now they have an enormous opportunity to take ATM and other banking functions to mobile phones without any substantial incremental investments.

Banks will use the mobile channel to provide an additional delivery channel to customers for convenience, comfort, control, visibility and security anywhere, anytime; to acquire new customers at significantly lower costs as the mobile phone adoption continues, since there are more mobile phone subscribers in the world than bank account holders; and to guard their eroding deposit base from non-banking competitors like merchants and online service providers.

Again, similar to telecommunication, banking has also seen its fair share of innovation in terms of underlying technologies and business models, with information and communication technology playing a significant role in its evolution. As banks started to grow in charter, servicing increasing numbers of users over a wider range of banking products, the need to bring about greater efficiency in terms of how its core banking functions were handled, how banks settled with other banks, how banks interacted with consumers and service providers, and how overall risk was managed across the entire ecosystem, became the driver for adopting new technologies.

Most technology innovations in banking focused on

the back end, delivering better core banking systems and better settlement networks. Over the years, the impact of technology started to creep towards the front end, with real-time transaction terminals in lobbies, ATMs, and eventually, Internet and mobile banking. That said, most front end channel technologies, having grown from the back end, most definitely lack a consumer-centric approach, sometimes raising obvious questions as to why it still takes a couple of days for a simple bank cheque to clear. Argued from the back end, it is perfectly well justified, what with a myriad of systems and networks that a simple cheque has to traverse, but with all the advancements in access and devices at the front end, it falls way short of expectations from a consumer's perspective.

In addition to the back end systems and channels, information technology has also played a significant role in the advancement of risk management methodologies and practices. The promise of efficiently spreading risk, increasing access to credit, and reducing the cost of capital has led to the development of a highly complicated securities and derivatives industry, all driven by complex algorithms and software, literally drying up the availability of mathematicians outside the highly lucrative investment banking and advisory industries.

With the crisis in the sub-prime mortgages industry in the US, and its snowballing effect across the entire banking

162

industry, there is increased scrutiny on the role technology has played in disrupting financial markets the world over, with a growing acceptance that the larger culprit could very well be the opaque systems and processes. That said, no one is denying the advantages of applying new technologies to banking in terms of delivering better products and better customer service, at the same time lowering the cost of capital.

With or without a crisis, what is undeniable and irreversible is the fact that banking has evolved from a local community-based strong-house and lending service to a highly comprehensive and integrated global financial service. If the recent events in the US banking sector are an indication of the future of banking, with the government essentially taking over several large financial services providers and forcing several others to merge to avoid a global financial meltdown, it may bode well for consumers and enterprises, as now they may avail themselves of various retail as well as commercial banking services from the same provider. Global banking is no longer an oxymoron but has become a norm to the point that once a bank grows to a certain size, it is forced to diversify and expand the world over just to survive.

With their enhanced footprint, banks have branched out into offering highly specialized products and services for consumers, enterprises and other financial services providers. With convergence of channels and cross-selling of services, banks also find themselves in a position to evolve from being just a fund provider to becoming a 'lifestyle management fund'.

As the world continues to witness the volatility of the banking and capital markets, first at the turn of the century, when the Internet bubble burst, and more recently, with the real-estate asset bubble bursting, it is becoming increasingly and painfully obvious that these growing opportunities come with higher complexities in terms of managing risk.

With telecommunication companies evolving into lifestyle management pipes and banks evolving into lifestyle management funds, merchants are rightfully evolving into 'lifestyle management providers'. In many ways, they were the first to build value-added services on top of their core offerings, quickly recognizing that there were larger opportunities in bundling services along with the goods they were manufacturing and selling. Examples range from an appliance manufacturer offering value-added services such as financing and warranties, to the iPod (and subsequently, iPhone) from Apple growing in prominence not only because of its revolutionary design but also because it comes bundled with a value-added service called iTunes.

With globalization, merchants, just like telecom companies and banks, see increasing opportunities for offering highly specialized products and services as well as increasing their reach to new and emerging markets. To leverage these new

164
.

opportunities, merchants are increasingly being forced to offer personalized products and services, supported by local business models, and leveraging highly optimized global supply and distribution networks.

As the telecommunication companies or lifestyle management pipes optimize their profitability, and banks or lifestyle management funds optimize their risk management, merchants or lifestyle management providers will be forced to balance increasing reach and differentiation with customer loyalty.

With the growing adoption of mobile phones worldwide, these three industries, namely the telecom companies, banks and merchants, have at times become willing, but in most other cases unwilling, bed partners. It is safe to state that no other innovation till date has brought these three industries together the way mobile telephony has. Hence it is imperative that all the three, while being cognizant of their strengths, do not lose sight of their weaknesses, and find ways to integrate their offerings without losing their individuality.

As consumers, we will always seek a common window for all three, namely a lifestyle management pipe, fund and provider, where one without the other is like trying to balance a three-legged stool on one or two legs. While the leather wallet has been that single common holder in the past, the m-wallet, or mobile wallet, will be the single common interface in the future for all personalized lifestyle transactions, in the real and virtual worlds, forcing all three industries to work together to deliver real value to the end users.

Over the years we have also seen several point solutions evolve for mobile phones, from minfotainment to m-commerce to m-ticketing to m-banking to m-wallet. As much as the early experiments have proven to be fairly successful, for these point solutions to scale they will require broader infrastructure support as well as a high level of aggregation.

Simply put, a mobile wallet will be adopted by the masses beyond the proverbial early adopters only if it truly mimics the leather wallet and adds value to it. Effectively, as consumers, in our mobile wallet we will seek the same level of simplicity, flexibility and security that we have in our leather wallets.

The service providers too will seek the same level of consumer control they have through their plastic cards and paper coupons. Set up and managed properly, the mobile wallet will enable providers to offer diverse services and service diverse markets, supported by different business and delivery models, consequently helping them increase customer loyalty, effectively manage risk, and enhance profitability.

Hence while simplicity and value-added services will be critical for consumers, customer acquisition will be critical 166 for the service providers. With the lifestyle management pipe, fund and provider truly collaborating to bring a high level of value addition to consumers, the mobile wallet will need a platform to support it at an infrastructure level, whereby it can effectively aggregate tokens, applications and incentives from the ecosystem without forcing the risk of one provider on to the other, and present it across all possible channels to the consumer through an extremely user friendly and intuitive interface.

Mobile phones initially appealed to users at the top of the demographic pyramid because of their exclusive nature, went on to become instruments of convenience for users in the middle of the pyramid, and finally became tools for sustainable development across the bottom of the pyramid. As a device, the mobile phone has evolved from a stoic brick-like form to a high couture wearable gizmo. But its larger impact will be felt in its service-level evolution, where from being a device to mobilize voice it has became a device to mobilize money, and is now evolving into a device to mobilize lifestyles.

Over the past several decades, the world has witnessed an unprecedented build-up in global infrastructure and communities, from telecommunication networks and related services providers to banking and settlement networks, from brick and mortar retailers to online merchants, and from large closed-loop systems such as the post office and railways to the New Age social networks.

With exponential growth in data-based connectivity and wireless networks, as well as the evolution of devices such as the computer, mobile phones and gaming consoles, the world has witnessed unprecedented access in terms of reach as well as personal access to technology.

From an enterprise perspective, the world has witnessed an unprecedented 'crossover' between relatively diverse entities, with telecom companies wanting to become banks, and banks wanting to become telecom companies. An Internet search company has become a potential threat not only to software providers but also to financial services providers, and a telecom company has evolved its infrastructure from connectivity to financial settlement and acquisition.

From an individual as well as a community perspective, the world has witnessed an unprecedented ability to create and distribute wealth, simultaneously creating imbalances between those at the top and the middle of the pyramid, and those at the bottom.

Riding this unprecedented wave of accomplishments, and in some cases embarrassments, in a highly connected and demographically diverse world with conflicting interests and priorities, is the emerging convergence of the lifestyle management pipe, fund and provider. This convergence, which we have termed mobile money, has several significant implications, the most obvious being leveraging mobile phones to replace cash-based transactions, followed by the integration of various lifestyle services on to mobile devices, and the possibility to help those at the bottom of the pyramid to gradually rise upwards.

If the ability to make payments using mobile phones is the engine, the various lifestyle management services are the drivers. What good can a virtual credit or debit or stored-value card on a mobile phone do for consumers and providers if there are no applications and incentives layered on top of these tokens that in turn will drive payments and transactions over mobile phones? While the underlying payment methodologies and associated risk management practices are critical, it is only when the lifestyle management pipe, fund and provider come together that the true and sustainable march of mobile money will begin.

10

The Future of Money

The mobile commerce and transaction industry has been in the making for many years, having had several false starts. Early experiments based on small phone screens and server-based wallets had very poor user response and were not scalable. To make banking, commerce and eventually, lifestyle management over mobile phones a reality, there are three fundamental requirements:

- Smart phones with bigger colour displays, Near Field Communication, and the underlying network infrastructure to connect over the Internet and download cards, tokens, and applications directly from the issuers – anywhere and anytime.

- Simple and intuitive user interface with the traditional leather wallet metaphor that incorporates branding and familiar images of cards, coupons and bills, providing the consumer with a single interface to easily access the plethora of cards and tokens, securely conduct a multitude of transactions in the real as well as the virtual world, and store electronic receipts to avail of various value-added and profile-driven services.
- High level of security to ensure that the infrastructure and service providers are comfortable, with the additional ability to directly reach out to customers and essentially, translate years of risk management practices developed over other channels seamlessly into the new and emerging mobile channel.

While elements of the above requirements are in place today, what is still missing is a common platform that brings all three together in a reliable and scalable manner. With respect to technology, the next frontier will relate to providing consumers with a highly personalized and user-centric interface, driven by (artificial and fuzzy) intelligence, which will bring applications to the user based on preferences and behaviour rather than requiring the user to go to applications. This would be supported by an underlying infrastructure so that transactions are managed more intelligently and presented in a highly optimized manner.

Based on our work on mobile money over the last ten years, we are able to connect all the seemingly irreconcilable technologies and trends to reach specific conclusions. If we were to distil everything down to select scenarios in terms of how mobile money will impact all the stakeholders, they would be read along the following lines:

1.0 In the near future, we will begin to see a whole new revolution around mobile phones – with respect to technology and commerce, with significant socio-economic impact – which will ultimately change the very concept of money.

2.0 It will begin first in Asia, especially in India and China, where there are more mobile phone users than Internet users or bank account holders.

3.0 The initial application will focus on mobile banking, to look at account information and transfer small amounts of money between various accounts; over a period of time, bill payment related to utility and others will become a major application; thereafter, adoption of other services such as ticketing, coupons, advertising, etc. would pick up, with mobile money becoming a truly rich and integrated application for consumer convenience.

4.0 The real explosion in mobile money will take place when NFC technology will be adopted to conduct physical world transactions, both for payment as well as non-payment services.

5.0 The adoption in the US and Europe will be delayed due to already available Internet banking and slow adoption of mobile applications.

6.0 If at all there is a single 'killer mobile application' beyond voice and messaging in well-developed markets, it will be cash-replacement over mobile phones with NFC.

7.0 Micro-transactions on the mobile will be the predominant application in the near term, ultimately leading to reducing the workload on mints for printing more money and punching more coins.

8.0 The use of ATMs will decrease, with the increasing ability of mobile phones to transfer funds from bank accounts to debit and credit cards.

9.0 Future banks with focus on mobile banking will be borderless and will require less brick-and-mortar infrastructure.

10.0 Mobile money will lead to paperless transactions and electronic receipts; every time there is a transaction, users will be alerted and informed with appropriate visibility and trail; tracking of receipts on mobile phones will facilitate tax filing and audit.

11.0 Over a period of time, all financial accounts and services will be integrated to provide a broader

173

picture of the individual's financial condition and net worth, with mobility enhancing overall financial management and clarity.

12.0 With more applications on mobile money, the risk and trust models will change substantially, supported by enhanced security and relatively less concerns on privacy.

13.0 The overall fraud related to the credit card business and related financial services will decrease, leading to (favourable) revisions to merchant discount rates, in turn leading to savings for consumers.

14.0 Mobile money will cause a reduction in the cost of transactions, owing to increased volume, disruptive business models, and greater transparency leading to relatively simpler settlement contracts and reduced legal and professional fees.

15.0 Mobile money will facilitate handling of multiple currencies, enhancing the movement of funds across borders or cross-border remittances, cross-border lotteries, and cross-border philanthropy.

16.0 Mobile money will lead to a global facilitation of microloans and micropayments between individuals.

17.0 Over a period of time, regional currencies will emerge in Asia, Latin America, the Middle East and Africa, with clear focus on two global currencies – the dollar and the euro.

18.0 Alternately, mobile money will enable providers to launch their own currency or transaction instruments, through closed and open loop settlement networks, supported by regulated treasury providers, and powered by a different business model through which payment transactions could potentially be subsidized by settling incentives and other non-payment applications over a common infrastructure

19.0 As mobile money proliferates with multiple currencies, financial services will be substantially deregulated worldwide over the next decade, significantly changing the role of the central banks.

20.0 More and more financial (and non-financial) services will appear on mobile phones in the next decade, with the mobile wallet metaphor driving adoption, and providing consumers with simplicity, convenience, security and flexibility.

In the miasma of all the technological jargon, people often lose sight of a fundamental consequence of the march of mobile money. At stake is nothing less than the very future of money as we have understood it for centuries.

To understand this, it is important to grasp two things. First, banks have always been slow to deploy new technologies, ideas, products, and services because of the risks associated with consumer behaviour, conversion costs, training, potential fraud, etc. And second, how money is earned, stored, spent and distributed.

As we understand it, the concept of money has changed substantially and has multiple meanings at multiple levels starting with barter, where goods and services were traded for transactions, to simple tokens and ultimately coins and currencies, which are a prominent mode of financial activities even at this stage. However, coins and currencies have changed significantly in recent times. For example, in pre-independent India of the 1940s, there were over thirty different kinds of currencies representing princely states. After independence, the national currency was issued to consolidate different currencies into one monetary instrument. Similar efforts gained momentum in recent times, when various national currencies were converted to the euro.

Thirty years ago, traveller's cheques were introduced to reduce risk while travelling. Thereafter, plastic cards were introduced in a big way for shopping, travel and borrowing. When plastic credit cards were introduced, people started spending money that they did not have, and a huge amount of borrowed money was introduced into the economy. This gave a whole new dimension to the concept of money – that of spending money that you did not have and did not really carry. In spite of checks and balances for printing money at various national mints and federal reserves, there are still cases of money laundering, counterfeiting, and black economy.

For example, to check trafficking of large amounts of cash across borders, many countries, especially the US, require you to declare if you are carrying more than US$10,000 into the country from abroad. In particular, the immigration form requires you to declare monetary instruments valued at more than US$10,000. Peculiarly though, law enforcement agencies do not recognize that credit card limits go way beyond the limit of US$ 10,000. It is believed that this is an effort to track the movement of money across the border. With money now beginning to reside on mobile phones, a lot of these regulations will have a different meaning. However, at the end, the concept of money is all about trust. Whom do you trust with your hard-earned assets?

Normally people get their money through salaries, sales, commissions, transactions, interest incomes, loans or a variety of other forms of financial transactions. People hold this money in the form of cash at home, in bank deposits, stocks, properties, money markets, bonds, gold, silver, insurance policies, retirement funds, certificates of deposits and other forms. They spend this money on buying products and services, and creating assets for their present and future needs.

With globalization and free market economy and emphasis on more and more privatization, the movement of money has increased substantially across borders. Whenever this happens, there are issues of exchange rates, cross border remittance, banking fees, wire transfers, etc. Today banks move trillions of dollars across accounts and borders through electronic means every day. To facilitate these movements, countries have their own federal reserve banks, local national banks, foreign banks, all conducting business with each other through a set of rules and regulations respected in various countries and across borders. There are also multilateral agencies such as the World Bank, IMF and other developmental banks, which facilitate lending and borrowing across borders to help development.

In the last fifty years, ICT, or information and communication technology, has had a significant impact on financial services, from back office automation, interbank transfers, ATM, etc. to improving efficiency of the movement of money. However, in spite of a great deal of automation and computerization, a substantial amount of paperwork is required for many routine transactions such as salary, bills, loans, etc. In fact, every expense generates paper receipts whose trail needs to be properly tracked for accounting and taxation. In the last decade, though Internet banking has taken root in major developed countries, its usage is limited in developing countries like China and India, where there are more mobile phones than bank accounts.

The fact that mobile phones will provide an incredibly valuable channel has never been lost on anyone, and over the

178

years, technology and service providers alike have continued to develop new systems, attempted to standardize them to realize interoperability and economies of scale, and have launched them in the form of field trials to further refine various services and solutions.

Once consumers begin to conduct financial transactions using mobile phones, the next step will be to integrate, customize and personalize cash, credit, loans, awards points, coupons and other promotions and incentives in real time, eventually leading to more holistic solutions that assist consumers with managing their individual lifestyles. The evolution, which has already started with relatively singular solutions like mobile banking, will be followed by other value-added services for the virtual and real worlds over a common interface, and will sooner rather than later be followed by true cash replacement.

Quite inevitably, the shift is caused by forces not only within the industry but without. The dramatic emergence of mobile telephony worldwide is fraught with enormous implications for the future of banking, and that of the form and concept of money.

It appears as if the disruptive effect of mobile telephony for traditional banking has not even been recognized by the banking industry, let alone planned for. Part of the reason is that the traditionally conservative industry is naturally reluctant to adapt to this dramatic change. The institutional

inertia is a serious challenge that this industry will have to address if it does not want non-banking players such as telecom companies and other service providers to gradually take over the role that banks have played so far. With the ever rising economies of stored-value cards, gift cards, coupons, and airlines miles, money that should have been parked with banks is now sitting with the issuers of such cards. It is safe to assume that this quasi-banking industry controls billions of dollars already. If the Gaps and Banana Republics of the world are sitting on millions of dollars in stored-value cards or gift cards, they are already, in some sense, usurping a function of the banks. This trend will only grow with the breathtaking spread of mobile telephony. People around the world will no longer find it necessary to park all their cash in banks. Instead they will have different instruments representing money sitting on their mobile phones. This has the potential to change money as we have historically understood it.

What seems likely now is that with growing numbers of mobile phones and supporting transaction solutions, consumers will gradually start spending more in bits and bytes and less in cash. This could happen in several different ways. As mobile banking gradually leads to mobile phone-based cash replacement in the real world, consumers will effectively tap their phones at a Starbucks and pay for a cup of coffee, redeem coupons, update their loyalty and send a virtual gift card to a loved one halfway around the world, all instantaneously; similarly, an American Airlines frequent flyer will not only be able to book and buy a ticket but also present a boarding card on his or her mobile phone at the airport. What is relatively straightforward to see is a day when a traveller taps his or her mobile phone to pay for a cup of coffee using a co-branded American Airlines and Starbucks virtual card, where the air-miles fund the card and pay for the coffee at an airport Starbucks.

Along with consumers and providers, the regulatory regimes will also have to evolve to embrace such inevitable scenarios. Will we as tax payers now have to account for our air-miles the same way we account for other sources of income? Will there be enough transparency in the system for us as consumers to see exactly how our private information translates into personal gain that is tangible and instantly gratifying?

As the underlying technologies get validated and refined, the next critical phase will be the evolution of scalable business models to ensure sustainability. For consumers and stakeholders across the value and delivery chain to truly benefit, telecom companies, banks and merchants will have to collectively drive various solutions. This is the only way to ensure a win-win situation for all. A common set of global technologies and standards will be required to enable aggregation of various services for consumers over a single and simple interface, and to allow providers to locally customize their individual delivery, business and pricing models.

As lifestyle pipes, funds and providers, all working together, truly start to leverage common platforms that provide a standardized set of technologies with flexible business models, consumers will become more empowered. Such a platform will remove disintermediation between the consumer and service providers, truly leveraging advantages of the advancements in ICT and the electronic/mobile channels.

A simple yet powerful example to elicit this would be paying bills. Irrespective of the market or demographic, every individual has bills to pay, either from his or her credit card company or utilities provider or possibly even in the form of a micropayment to a microfinance lender. In the old days, bills were typically issued on paper and sent by post, and most consumers would mail a paper cheque back to the provider. There is good reason why the expression 'the cheque is in the mail' has become immortalized.

With the advent of the Internet and online payment, a whole range of intermediaries evolved, from existing banks to third-party service providers, which reached out to consumers and the bill issuers, and citing advantages of ICT, essentially became a permanent fixture in the bill presentment and payment value-chain. As much as banks could rightfully argue that they were always involved in the settlement process, in the case of the current EBPP, or electronic bill presentment and payment processes, we could also argue that they have increased the disintermediation between the consumer and bill issuer.

Leveraging the unprecedented direct access mobile telephony provides, and using a common platform that truly allows the bill issuer to issue a bill wirelessly, securely and directly to the consumer's mobile phone, and that similarly allows the consumer to pay the bill using any of her or his existing payment accounts, will essentially take us back to the simple engagement models of bill payments from yore. At the same time, it will leverage the true benefits of ICT in terms of real-time issuance and settlement.

Mobile bill payments over such a platform provide the issuer the benefit of knowing exactly when a bill was issued and opened by the consumer, and similarly, allows the consumer to decide when to pay the bill and from which account. This would be a significant improvement on the current EBPP models, which force consumers to either predefine the account from which funds will be removed, or go to some aggregator's site to pay bills. Imagine the advantages to telephone companies alone, which can now issue bills directly to their subscribers on their mobile phone. For some inconceivable reason, mobile phone bills still continue to be largely immobile, with paper bills being printed, posted and mailed in the millions every day.

While empowerment of consumers in the instance of paying basic credit card bills may be limited, the impact such a system would have on the millions at the bottom of the pyramid and making microcredit payments, would be profound. Banks could actually use such a platform to directly reach out to trustworthy recipients, providing much-needed credit at a much lower rate of interest, as there will no longer be any disintermediation. For this demographic, every single dollar saved is an extra dollar in their pocket, with the potential of a better life for themselves and their families.

As banks have long known, the term unbanked does not always equate to unbankable; a more accurate term could be unreachable, where the banks find it difficult to actually reach out to the credit- and risk-worthy segment of the broadly labelled unbanked population. With mobile telephony and a common secure transaction platform, banks could reach out to a larger number of currently unbanked consumers. Once again, the impact of gradually replacing loan sharks currently filling the void at the bottom of the pyramid with regulated, institutional and socially accountable financial service providers would be profound.

The term bill payments has been stretched in the above example, but whether we call it mobile banking or mobile bill payments or mobile money transfer or mobile person-to-person or mobile micro-credit, the same case of lesser disintermediation and higher efficiencies, resulting in more dollars in the pockets of the consumers, can be made. The fact that the infrastructure deployed over the years, in terms of the pipes, the funds and the providers, can be easily leveraged to bring about these higher efficiencies makes the case for building a common platform even stronger and financially viable.

The empowerment and efficiencies are not limited to just the underprivileged section of the population; young urban users could feel more empowered if they could track their finances better; mothers if they could track their children better; brokers if they could track their portfolios better. Beyond individual empowerment, mobile money will also facilitate the 'crossover' phenomenon, where some day a bank could become a telecom company and similarly, a telecom company could become a bank. We have already seen how NTT DOCOMO, a large telecom company, diversified into providing financial transaction and settlement services, and is effectively trying to corner possibly two of the three legs that hold up the lifestyle management stool. While it is somewhat farfetched to conceive of a telecom company truly building up effective risk management practices in a fraction of the time banks took, it is definitely not an impossible task.

As if the friction between telecom companies and banks was not enough, online service providers have also thrown their hats in the ring. Google is feared not just for its ability to monopolize the search and advertising industries but due to the fact that with all the personal data it accumulates on users through its seemingly innocent search engines, it could potentially become a bank or a telecom company or (worse for the banks and telecom companies) make banking and connectivity free as part of its larger quest of reaching out to its core constituency of advertisers. With its absurdly astronomical market capitalization, it is not inconceivable that it might actually try to do all three.

As much as this scenario is highly exaggerated, the fact is that with mobile money, there is a real opportunity to create healthy competition with the right amount and nature of supervision and regulation, bringing higher efficiencies at much lower costs for consumers.

A more recent phenomenon of online social networks raises another interesting model. As much as the world has known social networks from the start of civilization, the online, and, more importantly, the mobile social networks will potentially provide the benefit of becoming large closed-loop networks in terms of managing risk. It is not difficult to envision offering qualified members within a social network, which already classifies and segregates users based on different criteria and preferences, more personalized services at lower costs.

186

As an example, consider all savings account members of

a large government-managed postal system interconnected by mobile money on a common platform. Not only can they conduct basic banking transactions but also access various value-added services offered by the postal network, and potentially start reducing, and eventually replacing, cash with mobile tokens. This will effectively become an extremely large closed-loop social network powered by mobile money, with the potential to become a true open-loop cash-replacement system with even larger and more far-reaching benefits.

Though these examples may appear to be extreme, they are definitely possible, and as much as their probability of success and sustainability can be argued, what is not so uncertain is that mobile money will increase access to capital as well as credit; that it will influence the cost of capital and drive it towards a true global standard; that it will truly alter the global movement of funds and potentially help even out imbalances caused by regional savings glut.

On a global scale, funds have traditionally flowed cyclically from the rich to the poor, and then from the poor to the rich. On a regional scale, funds have traditionally flowed freely into politically stable regions and not so freely into the unstable regions, limiting what the relatively stable regions could do to potentially assist the unstable regions. Mobile money will impact all these flows, with the potential to facilitate the flow of funds into regions where the return on investment is stronger, with relatively better immunity to these traditional barriers.

As mobile money proliferates, it will impact the politics of settlement, essentially reducing and possibly even removing the ability of middlemen to manipulate funds and related float between the different transaction initiation and termination points. It will impact the politics of establishing interest rates, definitely for retail banking and financial products, and eventually for rates that govern how banks lend to each other. It will impact the politics of how retail settlements fund investments in the underlying infrastructure, which in turn bring about greater transparency and accountability of how retail goods and services are priced for consumers.

With more than 3 billion mobile phones powered by a secure transaction platform running on top of trillions of dollars of communication and settlement infrastructure, with direct access to personalized payment and value-added services that are customized for different lifestyles and supported by a user-centric, as opposed to transaction-centric, business model, mobile money could truly be the decisive phenomenon that impacts regional and global inflation and recession cycles. It could impact regional and global fiscal policy and traditional savings and investment models, both at the personal and national levels.

Once mobile money is adopted beyond the critical mass – and it is not a question of if but when – what role will

the fiscal policy and regulatory regimes play? Consider a scenario where similar to a peer-to-peer online gambling service, which allows participating gamblers to establish the line, peer-to-peer mobile money users could potentially start establishing interest rates. Again, this may not be a question of if but when.

None of these is a doomsday scenario, but with the inevitable march of mobile money, it is important that all the stakeholders, from consumers to service providers to regulators, understand this phenomenon, and strategize, plan and embrace it to reap the benefits of being party to the unprecedented connectedness being thrust upon us.

With mobile money is it possible to conceive that we could have avoided a sub-prime mortgage crisis? At a very fundamental level, if the lenders could have direct and real-time access to the borrowers, could the financial world have avoided a meltdown of such a large scale? What impact could mobile money have on the food crisis the world is witnessing today? While mobile money would not solve all our problems, the power it holds is of unprecedented magnitude. How this power is channelled is up to all of us – consumers, providers and regulators.

11

India – The Power of a Billion Connected People

ndia today stands at an important phase in its development process. On one hand, it is a land of exciting and unparalleled opportunities, while on the other, it poses some daunting challenges.

While the challenges remain problematic, the prospects unleashed by the forces of liberalization, globalization and technology offer a unique window of opportunity. Technology, especially, is playing a key role in creating an empowered demographic. This is evident in the growth of mobile telephony, which has created a new power group – a billion connected people. This group is slowly but surely heralding a paradigm shift in the growth and development story of the country.

India has one of the fastest growing mobile markets in the world, servicing some of the savviest as well as basic demographics, catering to the most demanding as well as simplistic requirements, providing applications that can hog tremendous bandwidth yet balancing the needs of relatively trivial messaging services. This is being done by providers – telecom companies, banks and merchants – that have to continuously reconcile with the fact that while their average revenues per user are the lowest in the world, shareholders will continue to demand sustainable growth and profitability.

According to a report published in September 2009, the Telecom Regulatory Authority of India, or TRAI, estimated that India has over 470 million mobile subscribers, with over 120 million capable of accessing the Internet, but only 2 million active mobile web users. The number of bank accounts compared to mobile subscribers is significantly less, but with increasing consumerism, mobile value-added services have already started to pick up, and will continue to grow.

Indian providers – telecom companies, banks and merchants – have all started moving towards becoming lifestyle managers.

Despite being focused on the immediate goal of increasing their respective subscriber bases, most Indian telecom providers have designed their networks to deliver various services across multiple channels, related to content for the larger part, but building in the necessary scalability to support secure transaction services in the future.

Telecom companies have started to build an enterprise bus-based network infrastructure, which will allow them to aggregate and distribute content as well as personalized transaction services across multiple channels, ensuring a common interface for their subscribers and enterprise customers.

While sharing of network infrastructure across different carriers and outsourcing of managed services have got much attention from a cost-savings perspective, the coupling of a transaction management system with the existing content management system over a high-availability enterprise bus, supported by various vertical services and a community of secure transaction application developers, will enable carriers to generate new revenue streams, increasing their average revenue per user and enhancing revenue assurance.

Since there are more mobile phone subscribers in India than bank accounts, most major banks in India look at the growing mobile channel as a means to potentially increase their network and transaction volume. While banks in the West largely look at the mobile as just another channel in addition to their lobbies, ATMs, interactive voice response systems and websites, banks in India are looking at the mobile channel to acquire new customers by offering various time- and location-sensitive banking as well as non-banking services.

In several instances, the emphasis is more on non-banking services, like airtime top-up or recharge, ticketing, bill payments, coupons, and others, which in turn use the bank's payment products, indirectly converting users of mobile value-added services into bank account-holders and customers.

In their quest to provide banking services to the hundreds of millions of consumers in India who do not have any kind of account, banks in India have started several initiatives to promote financial inclusion.

The fundamental challenge with such initiatives has been two-fold. For a start, it is difficult from a cost perspective to provide the current banking services to those users whose ability to pay for the same is highly constrained. The larger challenge can be characterized as putting the proverbial cart before the horse.

If a consumer had the need for a bank account or banking services, and hence could justify the cost for the same, he/she would already have one by now. The very fact that a consumer does not have an account or cannot pay for the same implies the lack of such a need.

Hence it is critical that banks and other providers, and possibly even the regulators, first identify the services that will truly serve the needs of the masses, which in turn will justify the need for an account, possibly a stored-value account rather than a traditional bank savings account. Even if watered down in terms of features and subsequently the cost to service the same, the account will require a delivery model that can be scaled and a business model that can be sustained.

While financial inclusion is a moral necessity from a socioeconomic perspective and critical to India's long-term growth, it has to be driven by applications or services that will require a bank account or banking services, rather than the other way around. In essence, the approach of creating en masse bank accounts and forcing them on consumers cannot and will not scale.

Once again, this is where banks, along with other providers, have a huge opportunity. By leveraging various services related to mobile money, not only can they cater to existing account holders, but they can also start providing various services to consumers who currently do not have bank accounts and, in the process, start acquiring new customers.

While there are several well-publicized offerings related to mobile lifestyle services that go beyond the traditional voice and messaging-based services, such as providing farmers with weather-related updates and fishermen with market prices

before they come ashore to sell their catch, merchants or

service providers have also started focusing on leveraging the mobile channel to deliver personalized content, tickets, bills, coupons, targeted advertising, and other transactional services.

In addition to the top and middle of the demographic pyramid, the larger need and arguably bigger opportunities could very well be at the bottom of the pyramid in India. While understanding these consumers and their needs, and consequently providing catering services supported by the appropriate business models, is by no means a simple task, this is truly the next critical frontier for service providers.

These consumers at the bottom, similar to their brethren above them, transact all the time and have real needs that are not being met due to various factors. With the exponential growth in the number of mobile phones, access to these consumers and consequently the delivery model can get a huge fillip, which, when combined with mobile money, could become the silver bullet for financial and social inclusion, or more importantly, the means for building inclusive growth in India.

Effectively, financial and subsequently social inclusion will have to be initiated by merchants or service providers, first in identifying the appropriate services or applications, post which the banks can provide the necessary financial accounts and services to help facilitate the cash-in and cash-out for such services, leveraging the telecom companies' infrastructure for distribution; or, in other words, all three providers will have to come together to deliver this silver bullet.

Beyond financial inclusion, service providers in India are moving towards becoming lifestyle managers, operating across common platforms and networks, where carriers or telecom companies could focus on marketing and distribution, banks could focus on payments and risk management, and merchants could focus on delivering various products and services.

While the first wave, like in many other markets, was focused on launching vertical solutions, the next step is towards aggregating various banks and merchants across a common service provider-based delivery network and infrastructure, offering true mobile money services.

Because of India's large population, coupled with high density, there is literally no space inside-the-box; survival dictates that everyone continuously think outside-of-the-box here. Hence innovation is critical, and while there are lots of experiments under way, the true challenge is sustainability and scalability.

There are several examples of innovative mobile value-added or mobile money services. Airtel, India's largest mobile operator, distributes the bulk of its airtime through non-scratch-card-based channels; Indian Railways, one of the world's largest rail networks, allows passengers to book tickets through their mobile phones; ICICI, India's second largest bank, has been a leader in the mobile banking space, providing more than forty different features under its iMobile application; Tata AIG has launched an innovative mobile insurance service for its agents; Jet Airways, one of India's dominant airlines, has been providing mobile ticketing and related services through its Jet Wallet; Dainik Bhaskar, one of India's largest media companies, has launched a premium mobile content and secure transaction aggregation service called MeraMobi; India's National Informatics Centre has launched an innovative pilot that enables postmen using their mobile phones to distribute funds to recipients of the National Rural Employment Guarantee Programme, one of the world's largest social programmes, leveraging vernacular voice annunciation, biometric authentication and smart-card readers over Bluetooth; these are all examples of the innovative services being launched in India that truly leverage the growing mobile channel to offer various secure transaction services, solving real-world problems in a meaningful way.

Moving forward, service providers will continue to offer innovative mobile money services, driven by the applications that can add value to consumers' lives and, in the process, bring in further efficiencies throughout the ecosystem and related delivery value-chain.

One area ripe for further innovation is mobile P2P or person-to-person services in India. With the Reserve Bank of India's recent relaxation of its regulations related to fund transfer between individuals, several service providers have already started, or plan to start, services related to mobile P2P.

Beyond the obvious payment arena, this will also open up the avenue for person-to-person transactions through non-monetary tokens, such as coupons and loyalty, further linked to a cash-in and cash-out capability that is built and delivered as per RBI's guidelines.

Coupling the above with proven micropayment and microcredit services will enable more holistic integration of commerce and the availability of credit, consequently further reducing the cost of capital, both for personal as well as enterprise services.

With overall consumerism on the rise and the middle class in India having more dispensable income, there is a dire need for a mass-market credit rating bureau that can truly analyse risk on an individual basis, assigning a tangible score, which can then become the basis of creditworthiness and financing for various products and services.

Once again, the mobile channel could play an important role in this endeavour, with broad-based coverage and real-time access, enabling new and innovative models for managing risk, intrinsically linking the delivery of the service, with its associated transaction token, and its optimal trust model.

Healthcare is another area that can benefit immensely

from the mobile money infrastructure in India, specifically the underlying secure transaction capabilities. Delivery of clinical information, both for patients and providers, will carry a certain appeal in urban areas; rural areas could benefit from timely delivery of diagnostic toolkits for common ailments and tutorials for primary healthcare workers.

With postmen already equipped with mobile phones, the next step is to give mobile phones to all community healthcare workers or the traditional midwife, who till today is the critical link in the delivery of healthcare services in villages across the country.

The education sector, especially primary and vocational education, has already started to witness several innovative models emerge, helping scale programmes to build human capacity. Once again, the larger mobile money infrastructure could deliver personalized educational services, ranging from English language tutorials to tuitions for primary and secondary students to distributing standardized content for teachers in rural areas to toolkits for vocational education and job scheduling for various guilds.

Indian service providers have already caught the attention of enterprises all over the world, in terms of optimizing limited resources through innovative technology and business models, and bringing in further operational efficiencies, in the process providing sustainable growth and profitability.

Beyond resource optimization, Indian providers could very well become the global benchmark for innovative mobile money services, which leverage the integration of personalized content with secure transactions and incentives, delivered across multiple carrier channels and over a common infrastructure that aggregates the merchant and banking networks, offering services related to infotainment, finance, health, education and governance, to consumers across the entire demographic pyramid.

The Indian regulators – RBI and TRAI in particular – have done a commendable job over the years in balancing the needs of a large and complex demographic, despite the unique circumstances and constraints.

In recent times, RBI has been credited with navigating the Indian banking industry through the global financial crisis and TRAI has been acknowledged for making mobile connectivity more accessible to the masses.

While there will always be a few who will feel the regulators are at times too timid and conservative, especially when it comes to embracing new convergent technologies like mobile money, their prudence has been critical in ensuring stability and sustainable growth.

Moving forward, as various initiatives related to mobile money start to take off, Indian regulators will have to ensure that they provide the right level of guidance to existing stakeholders, without stifling creativity and innovations for potentially new and disruptive providers to evolve.

Assuming they succeed in a free market economy, these disruptive providers will not only be catering to a pent-up consumer demand but will also force the incumbent providers to operate differently, potentially reducing costs, and transferring these savings back to consumers.

Rather than being overly concerned about existing stakeholders and how their respective business models evolve as the mobile channel continues to proliferate, regulators should focus on ensuring that the right framework is in place to facilitate all forms of mobile person-to-person transactions, leveraging varied types of tokens, loyalty and applications.

It is safe to say that as we move forward, mobile money will mean different things to consumers and providers. At its core, mobile money may be reduced to a fundamental person-to-person or P2P transaction, which, when securely facilitated through a single and secure mobile interface in the real and virtual worlds, will not be limited by location or time.

Effectively, such transactions could be related to monetary services such as payments, or financial services such as micro-payments and microcredit, or pseudo-financial services such as coupons or loyalty, or applications such as health or education or governance.

Since it is not possible to envision all the different use-cases for mobile money, one plausible solution for the regulators is to create a framework for a superset of services, where essentially all other mobile money transactions become a subset.

One such superset service could be issuance of currency directly on mobile phones, effectively replacing cash without creating another cash-replacement product, and in the process enabling consumers to actually spend cash in the real and virtual environments using mobile phones. Such a framework could truly become the superset which could enable all the other forms of mobile P2P transactions or the building blocks of various mobile money scenarios.

Since true cash replacement cannot have any loaded costs, such a mobile phone-based currency issuance service would require a common infrastructure to enable other related transaction services – for tokens, loyalty and applications – that could potentially be issued, transacted over, and acquired through a common network, in essence subsidizing the cost of replacing cash.

Such a framework will not only enable RBI and its treasury partners to issue rupees on mobile phones, but will give the existing stakeholders the necessary guidance and regulation to build their own business models for mobile money services.

Additionally, this framework will ensure that the regulation and supervision is in place to stop a rogue provider from misusing or abusing mobile money for nefarious

activities. With the volatile security situation and increased potential for money laundering, India's geopolitical position unfortunately puts a larger burden on the regulators. But then again, this could be the silver lining that forces India to become the first frontier, further pushing the boundaries of mobile money.

India's telecommunication infrastructure was dismal, to say the least, thirty years ago. The government at the time embarked upon a very ambitious programme of building indigenous technology to meet India's unique urban and rural requirements. Supported by innovative business and distribution models that focused more on access than density, it took the country, which had less than 2 million telephone lines in the 1970s, to one of the fastest growing mobile telephony markets in the world today, continuing to add more than 10 million new lines every month.

While the first wave of innovations and mission-mode initiatives in the 1980s created the foundation for India's telecommunication as well as information technology industries, the initiatives over the past five years have turned India into a true knowledge economy, further leveraging its diverse and young human capital.

In addition to the physical infrastructure, the government has also made the necessary legislative changes, ensuring that every citizen has right to information and education. Coupled with the recent focus on sensitizing key stakeholders

– public and private – as well as the masses on the need for innovation, and ensuring appropriate policy and structural support for the same, the government hopes to create the right environment for incubating and building sustainable programmes that will drive innovation focused on human and social development.

With the information and communication technology (ICT) infrastructure largely in place, supported by the necessary knowledge-based initiatives and legislative framework, the government plans to leverage this foundation to expedite delivery of all public services, providing much-needed infrastructure and helping create employment for India's youth, in the process transforming India's demography, expediting development, and consequently reducing socioeconomic disparity.

Innovation will be required to expedite the delivery of public services for basic human needs related to clean air, water, food, sanitation, energy, housing, primary healthcare and education; optimizing the delivery of the ten to twenty services that impact citizens the most on a day-to-day basis; expediting the delivery of law, order, and justice; and eventually help convert ongoing e-governance initiatives to e-democracy.

Once again, mobile money could play a big role in the delivery of public services over this information technology

infrastructure, potentially creating employment and driving

entrepreneurship. New mobile money initiatives could very well provide the innovative and potentially disruptive new technology, business, and delivery models that could transform all of the above.

WEALTH CREATION & DISTRIBUTION

Mobile money also offers the potential to foster entrepreneurship across the New Age industries and create new employment opportunities for the small- and medium-sized enterprise sectors, both of which could be instrumental in delivering the last-mile solution for various e-governance services, in the process facilitating financial and social inclusion.

Just like other great civilizations, India has its own cultural DNA, where there is a method to the madness. In India's case this method is driven by an age-old philosophy of doing things because they need to be done, and not just because the outcome could be beneficial to the doer. The foundation for mobile money in India has been built by many such doers, some much celebrated and some unsung heroes.

With its deep cultural reverence for diversity, and given its unique position thanks to its young population and an emerging knowledge-based economy, mobile money could play a vital role in India's continuing evolution, providing the much-needed engine for growth as well as the critical arteries for distributing wealth across the demography. In the process, India could become the cornerstone for sustainable and scalable social development in India, and a beacon for the rest of the world.

Index

About the Authors

SAM PITRODA is an internationally respected development thinker, telecom inventor and entrepreneur who has worked for over forty years in the areas of information and communications technologies and their use as tools for human and national development.

Credited with having laid the foundation for and ushering in India's technology and telecommunications revolution in the 1980s, Pitroda has been a leading campaigner to help bridge the global digital divide. During his tenure as advisor to Prime Minister Rajiv Gandhi in the 1980s, he headed six technology missions related to telecommunications, water, literacy, immunization, dairy and oil seeds. He was the founder and first chairman of India's Telecom Commission, as also the chairman of India's National Knowledge Commission (2005-09), an advisory body to the prime minister of India that was set up to provide a blueprint of reform of knowledge-related institutions and infrastructure in the country. The commission has offered a series of recommendations on various aspects of the knowledge paradigm to help India meet the challenges of the twenty-first century.

Pitroda is currently advisor to the prime minister of India on public information infrastructure and innovations.

He holds close to a hundred worldwide patents and has published and lectured widely in the US, Europe, Latin America and Asia.

MEHUL DESAI has spent more than sixteen years in the areas of intellectual property, product development, business development, strategy and international operations, focusing on ICT and related applications across developed as well as emerging markets. He has done pioneering work in the field of secure transactions, with a focus on payment and non-payment services for mobile phone users worldwide.

As chief executive officer at C-SAM, Inc., a technology provider for mobile commerce, mobile payments and secure transaction solutions, Mehul Desai is responsible for C-SAM's strategy and operations worldwide. Prior to C-SAM, he held various engineering/R&D positions, working primarily in the areas of telecommunication, distributed systems and power electronics.

Mehul Desai is the co-inventor of issued patents and pending applications across several markets, including the US and EU. He often speaks at industry conferences on topics related to mobile commerce and mobile payments, and is involved with several start-up ventures and non-profit initiatives.